Aquinas & Modern Science

A New Synthesis of Faith and Reason

GERARD M. VERSCHUUREN

Aquinas and Modern Science

A New Synthesis of Faith and Reason

Foreword by
Joseph W. Koterski, S.J.

First published in the USA and UK
by Angelico Press
© Gerard M. Verschuuren 2016

For information, address:
Angelico Press
4709 Briar Knoll Dr.
Kettering, OH 45429
angelicopress.com

ISBN 978-1-62138-228-7 (pbk)
ISBN 978-1-62138-229-4 (cloth)
ISBN 978-1-62138-230-0 (ebook)

Cover Image: Jacopo del Casentino,
St. Thomas Aquinas, between circa 1325 and circa 1375,
tempera and gold on poplar wood
Cover Design: Michael Schrauzer

CONTENTS

Foreword

THE ETYMOLOGICAL ROOT of "school" is *schole*—Greek for leisure. Now, in many respects the time of one's formal schooling—especially at the level of college or university—is not likely to be a place of leisure. Even if one doesn't have to work to pay for one's schooling, the experience is likely to be busy enough—tests, papers, presentations, and academic activities of all sorts. What makes the situation worse yet is that there is little unity to most experiences of higher education. Unless one is at that rare sort of place where the coursework has been carefully fitted together, the experience is likely to seem busy in yet another sense—busy with many ideas from diverse disciplines competing for one's attention, and often one has neither the time nor the venue for sorting it all out. It can prove hard enough to keep one's head above water.

The present volume by Gerard Verschuuren just might help. *Aquinas and Modern Science: A New Synthesis of Faith and Reason* is designed especially for helping to unify an undergraduate education. It cannot claim to solve the problem of having to work to pay for one's education or the challenge presented by tests, papers, presentations, and other academic activities. But what it could help to provide is the leisure of mind that comes from taking a step back, to see how things fit together. The discipline of philosophy, especially in its classical thinkers, has a penchant for seeing the unity amid diversity, for formulating the principles that are operative in the practice of other disciplines, and for making explicit what often goes unnoticed.

Yet it is not just any philosophy that Verschuuren uses for this project. He takes up the thought of Thomas Aquinas, who undertook the projection of the philosophical unification of the most fruitful forms of knowing in his own day and who embodied in his own thinking the trait that is most distinctive of a wise

I

man: giving order to things. The need for intellectual order remains acute in our day. If anything, the task is more urgent, for the ramifications of academic specialization have proceeded at a furious pace, and it is ever harder to see how things fit together and how to formulate the principles that are operative in the practices of the contemporary academy.

Using his detailed acquaintance with a considerable range of today's sciences, Verschuuren here provides a thoughtful account of how the philosophical vision of Aquinas can help us to better see the unity of reality and to appreciate the wide range of scientific disciplines that study widely diverse aspects of reality. The book includes well-informed discussions of such technical issues as the indeterminacy problem in microphysics and the concept of randomness in evolutionary biology. For each issue, Verschuuren brings to bear the resources of the Thomistic philosophical method, clearly explained. To reach such a book, the poor beleaguered student will still have to find time away from working and from the other forms of academic busyness. But what it promises is a leisure worthy of a real education, the leisure of contemplation and of appreciation of the unity deep within the diversity of things that would otherwise seem too busy, too scattered, too diverse to be understood.

JOSEPH W. KOTERSKI, SJ,
Associate Professor of Philosophy,
Fordham University, New York.

Preface

WE LIVE IN a paradoxical time. Science enables us to know more and more, but it seems to be about less and less. This leads to some peculiar contradictions. Science allows us to reach into the outer space, but we seem to understand less about our inner space. Science enables us to create intricate machineries to direct our lives, but we cannot control ourselves. Science shows us more and more trees, but no longer do we seem to see the forest.

Is there a remedy for these contrasts? Yes, philosophy. Unfortunately, Albert Einstein hit the nail right on the head when he said, "The man of science is a poor philosopher." Scientists tend to stare at that square inch, nanometer, or micron that they are working on and feel comfortable with, while forgetting that there is so much more beyond their restricted scope. As the Nobel laureate and biophysicist Francis Crick put it, "They work so hard that they have hardly any time left for serious thinking."

Why philosophy? Philosophy has the power to bring clarity where confusion sets in. Philosophy has the capacity to create coherence where fragmentation looms. Philosophy can open vistas that no telescope or microscope can ever reach.

Why the philosophy of Thomas Aquinas? Because his philosophy has survived more than seven centuries. Its impact has gone up and down, but it always came out stronger than ever. It has been classified under various names—Thomism, Scholasticism, neo-Thomism—and has given rise to several schools, but its core has always stayed the same. It has been a beacon of safety in times of uncertainty, confusion, and tribulation. This should not create the impression, though, that vigorous debate does not exist among Thomists, but in this book I want to stay away from those discussions.

What made Aquinas's philosophy so successful? Probably the best answer is its timelessness. He took the best from another timeless philosopher, Aristotle. He did this so well that the world would soon take on his ideas, concepts, and distinctions—albeit with some, but not much, reluctance. Although he did not consider himself a purebred philosopher, but rather a theologian, much of his work bears upon philosophical topics, and in this sense it may be characterized as philosophical. His philosophy gained much ground in the Catholic Church in particular. In 1567, Aquinas was proclaimed a Doctor of the Church. In 1879, Pope Leo XIII decreed that all Catholic seminaries and universities must teach Thomistic philosophy. In 1998, John Paul II issued an encyclical called *Fides et Ratio* that reaffirmed the importance of Aquinas and his teachings. But the Church's preference for his philosophy is not exclusive but rather exemplary, making his philosophy serve as a guiding model. Also, this Catholic stance does not take away from the enormous influence Aquinas has had on scholars outside the Catholic Church, notably among Calvinists.

What could Aquinas ever contribute to our time, some seven and a half centuries later? One of the main reasons is that there are many similarities between his time and our time, between his world and our world. His thirteenth-century world was as turbulent as ours is. His world was confronted with an influx of new ideas coming from the Muslim world; our world is constantly being inundated with new ideas, coming particularly from scientists and atheists. His world saw the sudden rise of universities; our world sees an explosion of sciences and their subdisciplines. His time was marked by dubious philosophies; our time has been infiltrated by skepticism, secularism, and relativism. His era was a time of tremendous change; ours is also in permanent instability. His world had lost faith in reason; ours has too. Aquinas understood both the fascination of his contemporaries with new discoveries and new ideas and the very mixed feelings that come with all of that. So he most likely understands our time too.

It is no wonder, then, that his philosophy has been lauded by modern scientists and philosophers alike: scientists such as Albert Einstein, David Bohm, Werner Heisenberg, and Walter Freeman, and philosophers such as Elizabeth Anscombe (a student of Ludwig Wittgenstein and a prominent figure in analytical Thomism), John Searle, and Alasdair MacIntyre—to name just a few.

When I was teaching philosophy of biology at Boston College, the chairman of my department at the time, Joseph Flanagan, S.J., instilled in me that biology can only fare well with the right philosophy. I am sure he would have said something similar about any other science. That is why philosophy—and especially the sound, perennial philosophy of Thomas Aquinas—can be such a great asset to modern science. Aquinas addresses questions most secular institutions aren't even asking, much less answering.

For all these reasons, I would like to invite you on a tour through the richness of Aquinas's philosophy in an encounter with the sciences as we know them today. Let Aquinas be your teacher; let him give you a clearer and more coherent view of what modern science tells us. Aquinas's principles continue to serve as an anchor of intelligibility in a sea of confusing claims.

This book is meant to be a readable and wide-ranging introduction to the thought of Aquinas. I want it to be an introductory book for aspiring as well as accomplished scientists who are new to philosophy. It would even qualify as a textbook. Thus, I decided not to use citations or notes with references to my sources. For the same reason, the book is not exhaustive, let alone complete. Because its purpose is to open the mind of the reader to further study of Aquinas, I added some rather substantial bibliographies at the end of each chapter. They provide what the book leaves out. The selection is obviously limited and inevitably also one-sided.

I would like to extend a special thank-you to William E. Carroll, who expressed certain insights better than I ever could on my own. I am greatly indebted to his writings. I also wish to express my gratitude to those who inspired me during the writing of this book. In particular, I want to mention the physicist Stephen M. Barr, the philosopher Edward Feser, the Thomist John Knasas, the physicist Anthony Rizzi, and the biologist Francisco Ayala—to name just a few. Some of the sentences/phrases in this book are taken verbatim from suggestions or comments made by these individuals, but obviously, they are not responsible for the final outcome; if I erred, it is entirely my doing. They and many others make me realize that originality consists only in the ability to forget about your sources. If I was able to see a bit further at times, it was, in the words of Isaac Newton, "by standing on the shoulders of giants."

1

Aquinas and His Time

IT IS NO exaggeration to say that Thomas Aquinas was the greatest philosopher of the Christian Middle Ages, and perhaps even beyond. He put Aristotle's teachings in a Christian framework—he baptized Aristotle, so to speak—and changed Aristotelianism into what later became known as Thomism. Aristotle's writings were focused on the nature of knowledge, the natural sciences, metaphysics, the soul, and ethics, and they were packed with seemingly valid and convincing information and insights. Overall, it was a complete vision of the world developed without and before Christ—based on pure reason.

Aquinas's move of embracing Aristotle was very controversial at the time. At first glance, Platonism seemed more proper for a Christian approach, but Aquinas deemed it too otherworldly. History proved him right. Medieval theologians liked to say that the wine of Christian faith was at risk of being turned into the water of Plato, rather than the water of Plato into the wine of faith. Something similar could be said when it comes to science. Platonism would not have fit well in a worldview that would be increasingly influenced by scientific developments. But why Aristotle?

At the beginning of the thirteenth century, a wave of great historical change was coming over Western Europe as the works of the ancient Greek natural philosophers and mathematicians became available in the Latin language for the first time. This development caused great excitement among the Latin-speaking scholars in the then-new universities of Europe. They avidly pursued research in many of the natural sciences and essentially founded the historical tradition of experimental science that continues today. One of these geniuses was Aquinas. He wrestled with how Christian religion would be effected by the most advanced science of his day—the works of Aristotle and his Muslim commentators. Following in the tradition of Avicenna, Averroës, and Maimonides, Aquinas developed a philosophical system that remains one of the enduring accomplishments of Western culture.

Nearly two thousand years after Aristotle died, only a few of his works on logic had survived in Western Europe. But Jewish and Muslim scholars had preserved much of his writing. Starting in the twelfth century, these scholars brought Arabic and Hebrew translations of Greek texts into the West, and it was their subsequent translation into Latin that introduced Christian scholars to the works of Aristotle and others, making them available in the new universities that were forming. Learning had shifted from monasteries and cathedral schools to the newly established universities. Along with these translations came extensive commentaries on Aristotle. Since Aquinas—and most other scholars at the time—knew very little or no Greek, Aquinas asked his friend Willem van Moerbeke to translate Aristotle's Greek into Latin.

Why was the rediscovery and adoption of Aristotle's works so controversial? The Aristotelian explanation of the world based on natural law and reason initially seemed to challenge the teachings of Christianity. At first, the Roman Catholic Church tried to avoid his works. But some Church scholars, such as Albert the Great at the University of Paris, thought it was possible to combine human reason and Christian faith (see chapter 5). Soon Thomas Aquinas, his student, would devote his entire life to this task. Aquinas had ingenious insight regarding the potential that Aristotle's pagan philosophy had for Christianity and for an age of cultural and scientific innovations.

In Aquinas's day, the Christian world faced the greatest threat that it had seen in centuries. The threat to Christianity in the twelfth and thirteenth centuries was primarily the rising tide of Islamic religion and philosophy. The greatest philosophical thinkers of the Islamic world had combined Islamic religion with Aristotelian philosophy to produce a system that they called "integral Aristotelianism." The product of this thought became widespread during this time, and it greatly affected Christians. The key idea of this approach was called by its Islamic philosophers "double truth." The concept of double truth meant that a notion could be true in theology or religion and, at the same time, false in philosophy or science. A person was expected to go through life holding both truths—which were, in fact, contradictory. Aquinas could not accept such contradiction.

Aquinas addressed the problem by distinguishing between nature—known by everyone through general revelation—and grace—known by some through special revelation. He distinguished between those things that could be learned through the study of nature and those things that could be learned through the study of what comes to us by grace. He made a distinction between the two, but did not separate them—somewhere he said that grace perfects but does not destroy nature. In other words, we have in the Bible one source of information, about reality, and in nature another source of information, about reality. The Bible may provide information that is not obtainable from nature, and, vice versa, nature may reveal data that we do not know from the Bible. But those two sources of information, according to Aquinas, can never be in conflict with each other—as long as we understand them correctly. This distinction has also become known as distinguishing between the Book of Scripture and the Book of Nature. Its origin can be found in these words of Augustine: "It is the divine page that you must listen to; it is the book of the universe that you must observe."

Aquinas lived from 1225 to 1274. He was described by G. K. Chesterton as "a huge heavy bull of a man, fat and slow and quiet, very mild and magnanimous but not very sociable." His fellow Dominican friars referred to him as "the dumb ox," to which his teacher Albert the Great responded that "the dumb ox will bellow so loud that his bellowing will fill the world." Those words were prophetic. Although a man of profound humility and prayerful contemplation, Aquinas was also a pioneering genius whose writings constitute the apotheosis of medieval thought and the embryonic beginnings of a huge innovation.

Aquinas was born at Roccasecca, a hilltop castle from which the great Benedictine abbey of Monte Cassino is almost visible, midway between Rome and Naples. At the age of five, he began his studies at Monte Cassino. When the monastery became a battle site, Thomas was transferred by his family to the University of Naples. It was here that he came into contact with the "new" Aristotle and with the Order of Preachers, or Dominicans, a recently founded mendicant order. He became a Dominican despite the protests of his family and eventually went north to study, perhaps first briefly at Paris, then at Cologne with Albert the Great. It was Albert's interest in Aristotle that would strengthen Thomas's own fascination with Aristotelian thought.

Having returned to Paris, he completed his studies, and for three years he occupied one of the Dominican chairs in the Faculty of Theology. The next ten years were spent in various places in Italy, at several Dominican houses and eventually in Rome. From there he was called back to Paris to confront the controversy known as Latin Averroism and as Integral or Heterodox Aristotelianism. After this second three-year period, he was assigned to Naples. In 1274, on his way to the Council of Lyon, he fell ill and died on March 7 in the Cistercian abbey at Fossanova, some twelve miles from Roccasecca.

In the meantime, Aquinas had produced an enormous collection of writings, all in Latin. The title of Aquinas's most important work is given as both *Summa Theologiae* and *Summa Theologica*. This difference is probably in accordance with the spelling in the medieval manuscripts of this work. Most present-day Aquinas scholars talk about the *Summa Theologiae*. The other title is considered to be old-fashioned, but it is not clear why. It does not seem that Aquinas himself gave the title to the work. In any event, this book is probably one of the most cited works in the history of Western thought. The title suggests that it is about theology, not philosophy, but that might be misleading. Although Aquinas develops all of his philosophy in relation to God, his approach is mainly philosophical. In this book, we will focus on Aquinas as a philosopher, which may distort his fundamental theological reason for doing philosophy, but so be it.

In his books, Aquinas often uses a particular structure, rather common at the time. He starts with a specific question (*quaestio*), usually divided into separate articles. Each article contains arguments for and against a certain position. In the response (*responsio*), Aquinas explains his own position. Counterarguments are then given and, in turn, argued against. With this format, Aquinas models a core pedagogical technique used at the universities of his time—so-called "questions debated" (*quaestiones disputatae*). For this technique, students would take up sides of an issue, articulated as a question, and offer arguments for each side. The teacher would then evaluate the arguments and adjudicate. The fact that Aquinas structures many of his texts around this technique—especially his magnum opus, the *Summa Theologiae*—indicates that he wants students reading his texts to acquire not only the content of the view he himself supports but also the proper method for thinking an issue through and then arriving at a conclusion. A drawback when reading Aquinas is that we must consider whether certain statements are from him or from adversaries. This may have caused some confusion over the years as to what Aquinas really says.

As a philosopher, Thomas is emphatically Aristotelian. His interest in and perceptive understanding of Aristotle are present from his earliest years; they did not first appear toward the end of his life when he wrote some textual commentaries on Aristotle. When referring to Aristotle as "the Philosopher," Aquinas was not merely speaking metaphorically. He adopted Aristotle's analysis of physical objects; his view of place, time, and motion; his proof of the prime mover; and his cosmology (see chapter 3). He used Aristotle's account of sense perception and intellectual knowledge, but then made his own version (see chapter 4). His moral philosophy is largely based on what he learned from Aristotle (see chapter 11), and in his commentary on Aristotle's *Metaphysics*, he provides a cogent and coherent account of what is going on in those difficult pages.

Aquinas fitted Aristotle to the procrustean bed of Christian doctrine—but not without controversy. Aquinas's teaching came under attack, largely by Franciscans, immediately after his death. Dominicans responded. This had the effect of making Dominicans Thomists and Franciscans non-Thomists—Bonaventurians, Scotists, Ockhamists. The Jesuits were founded after the Reformation, and they tended to be Thomists, though often with a Suarezian twist. But the impact of Aquinas would hold out in the long run. When in 1879 Pope Leo XIII issued the encyclical *Aeterni Patris*—which called for a revival of Scholastic and Thomistic thought, at a time when its influence had begun to wane—the pontiff was not directing his readers to one school as opposed to others. Rather, Aquinas was put forward as the paladin of philosophy in its true sense, as one who both transcends and opposes the vagaries of modern thought since Descartes.

The response to Pope Leo's call was global and sustained. New journals and learned societies were founded, curricula were reshaped to benefit from the thought of Aquinas—and this not only in seminaries and pontifical universities, but in colleges and universities throughout the world. More recent giants such as Jacques Maritain and Etienne Gilson in France and Ralph McInerny at Notre Dame University may be seen as symbolizing the best of this Thomistic revival. Pope Pius X pointed out in 1907 that the defense of truth against false ideas is to be made through the use of Scholastic philosophy, rooted in Thomism. But when the Second Vatican Council came to a close, it was widely held that the council had dethroned Aquinas in favor of a smorgasbord of contemporary philosophical systems. But Pope Paul VI, who was the pontiff during most of the sessions of Vatican II, was very much influenced by the Thomist Jacques Maritain. Then in 1998, Pope John Paul II issued an encyclical entitled *Fides et Ratio*. In its reaffirmation of the importance of Thomas Aquinas, it may be regarded as the charter for the Thomism of the third millennium.

Because of all this, Aquinas holds a special place of honor in Roman Catholicism, and his influence has continued into the present. It is no surprise that among the writers mentioned in the *Catechism of the Catholic Church*, Aquinas is quoted more than any other writer with the exception of Augustine—some sixty-one times. To be sure, one can be an orthodox Catholic or Christian without following Aquinas's philosophy—indeed, his influence is minimal in Eastern Rite Catholic Churches and Orthodox Churches. And in the Western Church, not everyone follows Aquinas. Franciscans, for instance, generally prefer Bonaventure. Moreover, even those who consider themselves Thomists have various disagreements with one another and even with Aquinas himself.

Still, Aquinas's influence in the Western Church is hard to overestimate. Catholics refer to him as the Angelic Doctor. In many ways, Aquinas is the high-water mark of what has come to be called Scholasticism, or also classical theism. In fact, if you survey the writings on the doctrine of God, even those by Protestant Scholastic theologians after the Reformation, you will find that many depend almost entirely on the method Aquinas had laid out more than three centuries earlier. Today, many traditional Catholics, tired of the deviant innovations that occurred in the wake of—but not necessarily as a result of—Vatican II, look to Aquinas to provide a way forward. It is a safe, coherent system that trumps the incoherent amalgam of philosophies that we know nowadays.

However, a number of obstacles must be overcome if we are to appreciate Aquinas today. In Protestant cultures, he remains associated with an era that many believe to have been mired in barbarism and superstition—despite the magnificence of the medieval legacy, from the great cathedrals of Europe to the rise of the universities. Moreover, the influence of modern "scientific" atheism has led to the widespread belief that one must choose between faith and reason, and that faith is fundamentally irrational and opposed to science. This is an idea that Aquinas dedicated his life to resisting (see chapter 2).

If we can set aside our prejudices and approach Aquinas afresh, we may be surprised at how relevant his philosophy still is. The fact remains that he was a man who changed the world. So what can this person who lived more than seven centuries ago teach us that we have forgotten? Let us find out.

To open the mind for further study:

Bauerschmidt, Frederick Christian. *Holy Teaching: Introducing the* Summa Theologiae *of St. Thomas Aquinas*. Grand Rapids, MI: Brazos Press, 2005.

Chesterton, G.K. *Saint Thomas Aquinas, the Dumb Ox*. Dover Publications, 2009.

Copleston, Frederick. *Aquinas: An Introduction to the Life and Work of the Great Medieval Thinker*. Penguin Books, 1991.

McInerny, Ralph. *Aquinas*. Cambridge, UK: Polity Press, 2004.

2

Aquinas and Metaphysics

"METAPHYSICS" has become a highly ambiguous term. It has many, and very diverse, meanings. Some associate it with New Age philosophy. Some, at the other end of the spectrum, equate it with philosophy of science. And there are many other versions in between. Aquinas himself would say that metaphysics is the study of "being as being"—the relationship between the essence of something ("*what* it is") and its existence ("*that* it is"). Whereas the modern sciences study things as changing, Aquinas would say that metaphysics studies things as being.

These differences in opinion regarding the object of metaphysics have a long history. Unfortunately, the general outcome of this debate is that the word "metaphysics" has become a "dirty" word in the minds of many. It is believed to relate to what cannot be seen or felt or heard or in any way sensed. So this raises the question, What could metaphysics study that is not studied by physics, mathematics, or logic? The answer to this question is usually "nothing." Nowadays, most scientists, and even some philosophers, tend to stigmatize all those who hold an opinion different from theirs as "metaphysicians." It has not always been that way, and we need to find out why it need not be.

The Need for Metaphysics

It is very common to ask ourselves questions like these: Scientists produce knowledge, but what *is* knowledge? Scientists construct laws, but what *are* laws? Scientists study things—atoms, molecules, cells, genes, neurons, money—but what *are* these things? When scientists draw conclusions, they assume certain presuppositions without asking any further questions. Philosophers and metaphysicians, on the other hand, begin to question those assumptions. At those very moments when scientists are satisfied, philosophers and metaphysicians would begin to inquire further and search more thoroughly.

It could easily be claimed that there is no physics without metaphysics, or more generally, that there is no science without metascience. The sciences cannot be studied by the sciences themselves. In order to study the sciences, we need to stand back and adopt a bird's-eye view, so to speak—a so-called metalevel—which is in essence the level of metaphysics. Its goal is to observe the observer, to investigate the investigations, and to study the studies. This endeavor is a science in itself—a science of science, if you wish. Aquinas would most likely call this metaphysics.

The physicist Richard Feynman is often quoted as saying that philosophy—more specifically the philosophy of science—"is about as useful to scientists as ornithology is to birds." His statement might be taken as a final verdict on the usefulness of what we are trying to do in this book. But Feynman's comparison falls short and should not be taken too seriously, considering that the worthlessness of ornithology for birds cannot be blamed on the inadequacy of ornithology but rather on the incapacity of birds to grasp ornithology. I don't think that is something Feynman intended to say about the ability of scientists to learn from philosophy, even metaphysics. Arguably, science can learn something from philosophy, for the simple reason that there is no such thing as a strictly scientific level of disagreement, as distinct from a philosophical one. They are intricately intertwined. Perhaps Albert Einstein was right after all when he stated, "It has often been said, and certainly not without justification, that the man of science is a poor philosopher."

Yet, some scientists may even consider the above kind of reasoning a despicable form of metaphysics. Do they have a point? No matter what their opinion about metaphysics is, the fact is that no one can live without metaphysics. Those who reject metaphysics are in fact committing their own version of metaphysics. Rejecting metaphysics can only be done on metaphysical grounds, for any rejection of metaphysics is based on a metaphysical viewpoint regarding what the world "really" is like. Metaphysics may be a "dirty word" to some, but all of us are surrounded and affected by it. Opposition to all philosophy is itself an implicit philosophy. Those who reject philosophy and metaphysics are actually using some form of them.

What is the relationship, then, between science and metaphysics? Is physics the basis of our metaphysics, or is our metaphysics the basis of physics? Even a philosopher such as Bertrand Russell saw very clearly that physics cannot be the basis of metaphysics when he wrote, "It is not always realized how exceedingly abstract is the information that theoretical physics has to give. It lays down certain fundamental equations which enable it to deal with the logical structure of events, while leaving it completely unknown what is the intrinsic character of the events that have the structure. . . . All that physics gives us is certain equations giving abstract properties of their changes. But as to what it is that changes, and what it changes from and to—as to this, physics is silent."

Now if physics gives us only the mathematical structure of material reality, then not only does it not tell us everything there is to know about material reality, but it implies that there must be more to material reality than what physics tells us. First of all, this is a truth one cannot deny without somewhat affirming it, for denials don't have material qualifications such as being heavy or large, but instead immaterial qualifications of being true or false. Second, physics is about the material world, but in addition it needs immaterial entities such as logic and mathematics. Third, there can be no such thing as structure by itself; there must be something which *has* the structure. So, physics—and any other kind of science—is by its very nature incomplete. It requires interpretation within a larger metaphysical framework, and absolutely every appeal to "what physics tells us" presupposes such a metaphysical framework, implicitly if not explicitly. In other words, science does not determine whether metaphysics is right, but instead metaphysics ultimately determines what we can know and do know in science.

Nevertheless, there is a strong, persistent conviction among scientists that there is nothing more to material reality than what physics tells us. They believe that there is no worldview and no metaphysics in what they claim—at best, their metaphysics can be "reduced" to physics. They proclaim themselves "free" of any worldview, any viewpoints, any philosophy, any values. The technical term for this is *scientism*.

Scientism certainly was not a problem in Aquinas's time—it just did not exist yet. It is a rather recent invention—the indirect outcome of new philosophical developments since Francis Bacon, David Hume, and Immanuel Kant (see chapter 4). Supporters of scientism claim that science provides the only valid way of finding truth. They pretend that all our questions have a scientific answer phrased in terms of particles, quantities, and equations. Their claim is that there is no point of view other than the "scientific" point of view. They believe there is no corner of the universe, no dimension of reality, no feature of human existence beyond the reach of science. In other words, they have a dogmatic, unshakable belief in the omnicompetence of science. They portray scientists as a bunch of white-coated people—emotion-free and assumption-free—who battle collectively to wrest secrets from the stubborn universe.

A first reason for questioning the viewpoint of scientism is a very simple objection: those who defend scientism seem to be unaware of the fact that scientism itself does not follow its own rule—it is a nonscientific claim. How could science ever prove, all by itself, that science is the only way of finding truth? There is no experiment that could do the trick. Science cannot pull itself up by its bootstraps—any more than an electric generator can run on its own power. So the truth of the statement "no statements are true unless they can be proved scientifically" cannot itself be proved scientifically. It is not a scientific discovery but at best a philosophical or metaphysical stance or dogma. There is metaphysics again! There should be no space for dogmas in science, although they often do occur in the scientific community. This makes scientism a totalitarian ideology, for it allows no room for anything but itself.

A second reason for rejecting scientism is that a successful method like the one science provides does not automatically disqualify all other methods. The philosopher Edward Feser expresses this quite clearly: "But this no more shows that the questions that fall through science's methodological net are not worthy of attention than the fact that you've only taken courses you knew you would excel in shows that the other classes aren't worth taking." Scientism poses a claim that can only be made from outside the scientific realm, thus grossly overstepping the boundaries of science. If it is true, it becomes false. It steps outside science to claim that there is nothing outside science and that there is no other point of view—which does not seem to be a very scientific move. Paul Feyerabend, the late philosopher of science at the University of California, Berkeley, came to the opposite conclusion when he said that "science should be taught as one view among many and not as the one and only road to truth and reality." The late British analytical philosopher Gilbert Ryle phrased this idea in his own terminology: "The nuclear physicist, the theologian, the historian, the lyric poet and the man in the street produce very different, yet compatible and even complementary pictures of one and the same 'world.'"

A third reason for questioning scientism is the following. Scientific knowledge does not even qualify as a superior form of knowledge; it may be more easily testable than other kinds, but it is also very restricted and therefore requires additional forms of knowledge. Mathematical knowledge, for instance, is the most secure form of knowledge, but it is basically about nothing. Consider this analogy: a metal detector is a perfect tool for locating metals, but there is more to this world than metals. An instrument can detect only what it is designed to detect. That is exactly where scientism goes wrong: instead of letting reality determine which techniques are appropriate for which parts of reality, scientism lets its favorite technique dictate what is considered "real" in life—and it is thus in denial of the fact that science has purchased success at the cost of limiting its ambition. To best characterize this attitude, we might borrow an image from the late psychologist Abraham Maslow: If you have only a hammer, every problem begins to look like a nail. So we should be careful not to idolize our scientific hammer, because not everything is a nail. Even if we were to agree that the scientific method gives us better testable results than other sources of knowledge, this would not entitle us to claim that only the scientific method gives us genuine knowledge of the world around us.

A fourth argument is that science is about material things but requires immaterial things such as logic and mathematics. If logic is just a movement in the brain of a bewildered ape, good logic should be as misleading as bad logic. Logic and mathematics are not physical and therefore not testable by naturalistic science—and yet they cannot be denied by science. In fact, science relies on logic and mathematics to interpret the data that scientific observation and experimentation provides. Logic and reason are perfect examples of the immaterial phenomena that we all know exist but that naturalistic science cannot measure. These immaterial things are real and demonstrable, yet they are outside of scientific observation.

A fifth argument against scientism is that no science, not even physics, is able to claim a superior form of knowledge. Some scientists may argue, for example, that physics always has the last word in observation, for the observers themselves are physical. But why not say then that psychology always has the last word, because these observers are interesting psychological objects as well. Neither statement makes sense; observers are neither physical nor psychological, but they can indeed be studied from a physical, biological, psychological, or statistical viewpoint, which is an entirely different matter. The findings of science are always fragmentary. Limiting oneself to a particular viewpoint is in itself at best a metaphysical decision. However, to quote Shakespeare, "There is more between Heaven and Earth than dreamt of in your philosophy."

A sixth argument against scientism is that the very pioneers of science in England were very much aware of the fact that there is more to life than science. When the Royal Society of London was founded in 1660, its members explicitly demarcated their area of investigation and fully understood that they were going to leave many other domains untouched. In its charter, King Charles II assigned to the fellows of the Royal Society "the privilege of enjoying intelligence and knowledge," but with the following important stipulation "provided in matters of things philosophical, mathematical, and mechanical." That's how the domains of knowledge were separated; it was this "partition" that led to a division of labor between the sciences and other fields of human interest. By accepting this separation, science bought its own territory, but certainly at the expense of all-inclusiveness; the rest of the "estate" was reserved for others to manage. On the one hand, this separation gave to scientists all that could "methodically" be solved by dissecting, counting, and measuring. On the other hand, these scientists agreed to keep their hands off of all other domains—education, legislation, justice, ethics, philosophy, religion, etc.

If the aforementioned arguments are valid, it is hard to believe, let alone defend, that physics is the basis of metaphysics. It seems more warranted to take the reversed position, namely, that metaphysics is at the basis of physics, and of all the other sciences. Only metaphysics can help us understand where science stands by taking a metalevel view. Albert Einstein was right when he said, "The more I study physics, the more I am drawn to metaphysics." Science cannot operate without metaphysics—that is, without certain convictions or principles regarding what nature is like. Scientists assume, for instance, that this universe is intelligible for us, and that it is a universe of "law and order." In addition, they all hold metaphysical positions that determine what the basic elements in this universe are supposed to be. Because of all this, even science is a metaphysics-based enterprise. It is only in trusting that nature is law-abiding and intelligible that scientists have reason to trust their own scientific reasoning.

Faith and Reason

Those who think there isn't any space left for *philosophy* outside the domain of science most likely also believe that science does not leave any room for *religion*. Fortunately, metaphysics is able to clarify not only the relationship between science and philosophy, but also the relationship between science and religion. What does Aquinas have to say about this?

Much of what is currently discussed under the science-and-religion heading Aquinas would have seen as part of a larger problem—that of the relationship between faith and reason. As we saw earlier, in Aquinas's time, there were advocates of the so-called "double truth theory," which held that the "truths" of philosophy and science were in one category and the "truths" of faith and religion in another. With this interpretation, one can hold mutually exclusive positions as long as one believes that the opposing views were in separate departments of the mind. Aquinas considered this view untenable. He saw with utter clarity that since all truth comes from God, there can never be, ultimately, any conflict between the outcome of reason and the beliefs of faith, or between the data of the sciences and the facts of revelation, or between philosophical truths and theological truths.

Aquinas's conception is quite radical. What we know through reason can never be in conflict with what we know through faith, and what we know through faith can never be in violation of what we know through reasoning. Nevertheless, some people think that when we begin to use reason, we have no choice but to abandon faith; conversely, some think that if we have faith, we must leave reason behind. Aquinas argues the opposite. We should be faithful in our reasoning and reasonable in our faith— even when, or specifically when, it comes to God. We cannot live by faith alone or by reason alone, but only by a harmonious combination of faith *and* reason. Sometimes we need understanding before we can believe; at other times we need faith before we can understand. Aquinas demonstrated that a natural harmony exists between faith and reason. Hence, what seems to be reason that is incompatible with faith is not reason, and what seems to be faith is not faith insofar as it is opposed to true rationality. Thus, Aquinas created a new synthesis, which would shape culture throughout the following centuries. It could be called the "Grand And"—a match made in heaven.

Aquinas sees reason and faith as two ways of knowing. "Reason" covers what we can know by experience and logic alone. From reason, he would say, we can know that there is a God; this truth about God is accessible to anyone by experience and logic alone, apart from any special revelation from God (see chapter 3).

"Faith," on the other hand, covers what we can know thanks to God's special revelation to us—which comes through the Bible and Judeo-Christian tradition. By faith, we can know, for instance, that God came into the world through Jesus Christ and that God is triune (Father, Son, and Holy Spirit). These truths about God cannot be known by reason alone. Yet, faith builds on reason and must be compatible with reason. Since faith and reason are two different ways of arriving at truth—and since all truths are harmonious with one another—faith is consistent with reason. If we understand faith and reason correctly, according to Aquinas, there will be no conflict between what faith tells us and what reason tells us.

Aquinas is very definite in defending the idea that faith cannot be against reason. When something is against reason, God cannot create it. Aquinas is so adamant on this issue because God is reason, so He cannot act against His own nature by doing what is contradictory. God is absolutely free, but His freedom is not arbitrary, so He cannot go against what is true and right. We know this, because our own power of reason is rooted in creation and thus participates in God's power of reason. As a consequence, God's omnipotence does not mean that God is able to do what is logically contradictory. Aquinas gives many examples: God cannot create square circles; God cannot make someone blind and not blind at the same time; God cannot declare true what is false; God cannot undo something that happened in the past; and the list goes on and on. To use a silly example: God does not even have the power to make a stone so heavy that He Himself cannot lift it—that would be contradictory, and therefore against reason.

The distinction between faith and reason can be carried over to the distinction between theology and philosophy. Aquinas clearly distinguished theology from philosophy. Theology gives us knowledge through faith and revelation, whereas philosophy gives us knowledge through the natural powers of the intellect common to all people. Thus, Aquinas held that theology and philosophy proceed according to different paths. Theology concerns itself with knowledge that has been revealed by God and that man must accept in faith. Philosophy, at least as defined by Aquinas, is concerned with knowledge that humans acquire through sensory experience and the use of the natural light of reason.

This distinction provides a formal test for deciding whether a discourse is philosophical or theological. If it relies only on truths that anyone is able to know about the world, after due reflection, and if it leads to new truths on the basis of such truths, and only on that basis, then it is philosophical discourse. On the other hand, discourse based on our accepting as true that there are three Persons in one divine nature, that our salvation was effected by the sacrifice of Jesus, that Jesus is one Person but two natures, and the like, is theological discourse. Yet, it remains true that theological discourse could and should never be in conflict with reason.

Times have changed. Nowadays, many tend to restrict what we know through reasoning to what we know from *science*, and what we know through faith to what we know from *religion*. So the twosome "faith and reason" is often narrowed down to the twosome "science and religion." But even then, Aquinas keeps insisting that faith and reason both deal with their own type of truth—with all truth ultimately coming from God. Translated into terms of science and religion, there are truths about nature and there are truths about revelation. Science has theories to help us understand nature, but they are subject to change—so we should not make science more than what it is. Religion, on the other hand, has truths to help us understand God, but they never change—so we should not make religion less than what it is. Religion reveals to us truths that no science can reach. But there cannot be any real conflicts between the two. Science tries to reach the truth but has not fully captured it yet. Religion, on the other hand, has the truth but has not fully understood it yet.

If there are apparent conflicts between science and religion— to use our modern distinction—then they are born of either bad science or bad religion, and they should compel the puzzled thinker to dig deeper and think harder. Following Augustine, Aquinas said that if an interpretation of the Bible runs counter to clearly established findings of the sciences, we should move to a more mystical and symbolic reading of the scriptural passage.

Conversely, we might add, when so-called scientific claims run counter to reasonable faith, they must have overstepped the boundaries of science and should be reexamined.

However, to the popular, biased mind of this age, the Galileo affair is prima facie evidence that the free pursuit of truth became possible only after science had "liberated" itself from the religious and theological shackles of the Middle Ages. Needless to say, Aquinas would see this as a false contrast. Even Galileo himself realized that he did not have enough evidence for his heliocentric model at the time. For instance, he could not answer the strongest argument against it, which had been made nearly two thousand years earlier by Aristotle himself. If the earth did orbit the sun, the ancient philosopher wrote, then stellar parallaxes would be observable in the sky. In other words, there would be a shift in position of a star observed from the earth on one side of the sun, and then six months later from the other side. However, given the limited technology of Galileo's time, no such shifts could be observed. It would require more-sensitive measuring equipment than was available in Galileo's day to document the existence of these shifts, given the stars' great distance. This lack of evidence was one of the main reasons why the respected astronomer Tycho Brahe had refused to fully adopt Copernicus's model. The case was not decided until 1838, when Friedrich Bessel succeeded in determining the parallax of the star sixty-one Cygni.

Galileo was well aware of this lack of evidence for his heliocentric system; he even admitted that no experiment performed on the earth could serve as a proof of its motion at the time. Other "facts" also seemed to confirm that the earth did not move, for if it did, the clouds would be left behind—a "fact" that Galileo himself had already noted in a lecture of 1601. Besides, Galileo had to concede in a letter to Johannes Kepler that many people were unable to see what they were "supposed" to see through his telescope. Yet, Galileo was so determined to find much-needed proof for his heliocentrism that he probably was blind to any inconsistencies—at least that is the impression Albert Einstein had. In his desperation, Galileo came up with his theory of the tides, which purported to show that the tides are caused by the rotation of the earth. Even some of Galileo's friends could see that this was patent nonsense, but Galileo plainly rejected the idea that the moon was a causal factor here.

Nevertheless, Galileo refused to present his theory as merely a hypothesis instead of established truth. He refused the reasonable alternative that the Church offered him—that Copernicanism might be considered a hypothesis, until further proof could be given. It is as if Aquinas had foreseen all of this almost four centuries earlier. He had already noticed that the visible motions of the celestial bodies "are produced either by the motion of the object seen or by the motion of the observer. . . . [It] makes no difference which one is moving." In other words, the sun could be moving, or we could be moving. Elsewhere, Aquinas states, "The suppositions that these men [Ptolemaic astronomers] have invented need not necessarily be true: for perhaps, while they save the appearances under these suppositions, they might not be true. For maybe the phenomena of the stars can be explained by some other schema not yet discovered by men." Apparently, Aquinas understood that the Ptolemaic theory was just that, a theory, and that there could be other theories and explanations.

Often the "Galileo case" is portrayed as a conflict between natural explanations and supernatural explanations. As the nuclear physicist Stephen M. Barr rightly observes, "The geocentric theory that the Church in effect endorsed was no more supernatural than the heliocentric theory that it condemned. This was a clash between two perfectly naturalistic theories of astronomy. It was the veracity of Scripture that the Church authorities (mistakenly) saw themselves as upholding, not supernatural explanations of planetary motion over natural ones. . . . The Scientific Revolution of the seventeenth century had to overcome the naturalism of Aristotle, not the supernaturalism of Christianity."

All of this makes clear how sound Aquinas's principle of "faith and reason" is. Faith and reason—or science and religion, for that matter—are not in a power struggle; they in fact need each other. This does not mean, though, they should merge together. A harmonious combination is not the same as a complete fusion. Nevertheless, some people like to mix science and religion together into one single concoction—which is like mixing water and oil. They tend to speak in terms of "reconciliation," as if science and religion were just two different ways of expressing the same truth. Such people basically want to "reconcile" the data of religion with the data of science. They want to fuse two different perspectives into one. However, if you mix them together, the result can go in two opposite directions: either science annexes religion or religion takes over science.

The most common outcome of a fusion between science and religion is that science annexes religion—that is, it "interprets" the data of religion so as to leave the data of science intact, since scientific facts are considered to be "safe" and "proven." Hence, new scientific developments are supposed to lead to a revamping of religious doctrine. However, there is no reason why religion should bend to the criteria of science. What gives science that authority? Science cannot claim such authority. First of all, science is not omni-competent. Second, what we call "proven" scientific knowledge is only proven until a new set of empirical data "disproves" what was previously considered "proven." In science, whatever is true today may not be true tomorrow. Science is always a work in progress.

Nevertheless, some scientists cannot resist the temptation to claim certainty and finality. The Dutch physicist Pieter Zeeman, later to become a Nobel laureate, was fond of telling how in 1883, when he had to choose what to study, people had strongly dissuaded him from studying physics. "That subject's finished," he was told, "there's no more to discover." It is even more ironic that this also happened to Max Planck, since it was he who, in 1900, laid the foundations for one of the greatest leaps in physics, the quantum revolution. And as if scientists never learn, Stephen Hawking ended an inaugural lecture some years ago by stating that it is quite possible that physics is almost finished. Apparently, it remains a timeless temptation to claim that the unknown has been reduced to nothing, or at least almost nothing. However, the magnitude of the unknown is, well… unknown!

The second possible outcome of a fusion between science and religion is that religion conquers and suppresses science by giving scientific data a religious allure. But such a route is dangerous as well; it has been tried out many times, most recently by proponents of creationism—"the Bible is right and science is wrong"—

or by fans of "Intelligent Design Theory," who claim that scientific processes sometimes need periodic divine interventions (see chapter 9). We have another attempt here to create a mixture of "oil and water"; but again, these two just do not mix well together. Religion is very different from science. What is true in Catholicism today will also be true tomorrow. But not so in science. Science works through experiments; what is true today may have to be revised tomorrow. The bottom line is that if we do not honor the separation Aquinas makes, science will become a pseudo-religion and religion will become a semi-science. The scientist must submit his mind to the data of experiment; the theologian must submit his to the data of revelation.

All these discussions sound very metaphysical. So it is time now to ask the key question: Can metaphysics do all of the above for us? Some modern philosophers express their doubts, as we saw already. They keep denying the legitimacy of metaphysics, period. Those who do so adhere in fact to a materialist position, claiming that metaphysics has no distinctive subject because its subject falls outside the "material" on which the natural sciences—sometimes called the "hard" sciences—focus. But, ironically, so does science itself; it is an enterprise that also falls outside the material realm studied by the natural sciences, for science is certainly not a material entity in itself.

So what does metaphysics achieve, then, to make science a legitimate enterprise? Whereas the natural sciences look at material beings, metaphysics looks at universal properties and laws and principles—such as what it means to be a *being*, and related questions. In the words of Martin Heidegger, Western metaphysics is guilty of a "forgetfulness of being" because the natural sciences focus on *what* things are, thus forgetting to think about the fact *that* they are. Aquinas does take this latter issue into consideration. The primacy of the act of existence is at the very center of his view of metaphysics, as we will soon find out.

So we need some terminological clarification here. What Aquinas calls "metaphysics" is a science of "being as such," which he differentiated from "physics," the science that concerns itself with material or changeable being. The term "metaphysics" can be traced back to Aristotle. The prefix meta ("after") indicates that these works of Aristotle come "after" the chapters on physics. However, Aristotle himself did not call the subject of these books "metaphysics"—he referred to it as "first philosophy." The editor of Aristotle's works, Andronicus of Rhodes, is thought to have placed the books on "first philosophy" right after another work, *Physics*, and then called them "the books that come after the [books on] physics." This was misread by some Latin scholars, who thought it meant "the science of what is beyond the physical."

A person who studies metaphysics is called a metaphysicist, or a metaphysician. The metaphysician attempts to clarify the fundamental notions by which people understand the world—notions such as essence and existence, objects and their properties, space and time, cause and effect, actuality and possibility. A central branch of metaphysics is ontology, the investigation into the basic categories of being and how they relate to one another. Another central branch of metaphysics is the study of the origin and the fundamental structure, nature, and dynamics of the universe—sometimes called "philosophy of nature."

The intriguing question first posed by the philosopher G. W. Leibniz some three centuries ago was, "Why is there something rather than nothing?" It was Martin Heidegger who woke us up again from our "positivist slumbers" by opening his book *An Introduction to Metaphysics* with the same question that Leibniz had. It is in this arena, ahead of his time, that Aquinas, in the footsteps of Aristotle, developed his philosophical system. One of its main goals was to analyze the "principles of nature." These principles are basic, fundamental distinctions or classifications that we will discuss in the next chapter. They are like assumptions that we cannot empirically corroborate or logically derive from anything else but that we need in order to understand nature. Ironically, many scientists have a PhD, a "doctorate of philosophy," but they have forgotten about the philosophy behind their science. It is Aquinas's metaphysics that can provide science with a foundation that science cannot provide on its own.

To open the mind for further study:

Carlson, John W. *Understanding Our Being.* Washington, DC: Catholic University of America Press, 2008.

Feser, Edward. *Scholastic Metaphysics: A Contemporary Introduction.* Editiones Scholasticae, 2014.

Knasas, John F.X. *Being and Some Twentieth-Century Thomists.* New York: Fordham University Press, 2003.

Kreeft, Peter. *A Summa of the Summa.* Ignatius Press, 1990.

3

Aquinas and Nature's Principles

WHAT DOES Aquinas mean when he speaks of "principles of nature"—for instance, in his book *De Principiis Naturae*? These principles are probably best understood as something like starting points or assumptions, not themselves the products of empirical induction or of deductive proof, and thus they are said to be known "by themselves"—which does not mean of course that they are exempt from rational analysis and inquiry. So do not confuse universal principles in metaphysics with general statements in science such as "all iron expands with heat." The latter are confirmed by, for example, testing more and more instances of iron under various temperature conditions; such cases are examples of generalization. In contrast, universal principles such as "all expanding of iron has a cause" are true, independently of any particular cases; their truth does not increase by testing more and more instances, because their truth does not depend on generalization.

It is important to realize that Aquinas's universal principles in metaphysics are different from generalizations in science. These universal principles are not like scientific hypotheses that require verification or falsification. They are not something we see over and over again, but they are principles that *make* us see. They come *before* we can experience anything else; without them, there are just no experiences. They are true independently of any cases in particular, and they do not become more corroborated with an increasing number of supporting cases. When Aquinas speaks of "principles of nature," he is not speaking science but metaphysics. The good part is that we are capable of grasping the truth of these universal principles without the assistance of science. Their truths are accessible to everyone, whereas the truths of science we must often receive from others, in faith.

What may discourage some people from studying Aquinas, though, is that he uses terms and distinctions that seem rather outlandish to a modern reader and would need some further explanation. It may seem at first that you are entering a world rather foreign to you, but once you have become familiar with that world, the rest of this book will show you how fruitful and insightful your pursuit may be.

So let us just explain the basics. The most pivotal "principles of nature" are essence and existence, act and potency, matter and form, substance and accidents, fivefold causality, and primary and secondary cause. Again, not one of them qualifies as a scientific hypothesis; instead, they are universal, metaphysical principles. We will briefly discuss them here—certainly too briefly, since Aquinas analyzes them extensively and very thoroughly. Just by looking at the kinds of questions Aquinas raises and answers in his *Summa Theologiae*, one can immediately sense that no detail was considered too small or "nitpicky" to have a disagreement about. Nevertheless, we will only discuss them insofar as they are needed to understand the rest of this book. If you find these concepts still too complicated, you can perhaps skip this chapter until a further need arises. It is more like a brief course for beginners. But an imperfect exposure to a sound philosophy is far better than a full exposure to an unsound one.

Esse, Essence, Existence, and Substance

"To be, or not to be, that is the question"—not only in *Hamlet* but also in the philosophy of Aquinas. Everything has two principles that explain its being (*esse*): essence (*essentia*) and existence (*existentia*). In all finite beings, these principles are both required in order for the actually existing individual thing to be. Essence may be described as the "what" of a thing, that which is known about it by our forming of a concept. It is a universal principle making many material individuals to be of the same kind.

But, it is obvious upon reflection that *"what* a thing is" and "*that* it is" are completely different statements. Aquinas emphasizes that just because something has an essence doesn't guarantee its existence. Anyone can understand what a unicorn or mermaid is, and yet not know whether or not these exist in reality. Therefore, it is evident that the act of existing is different from essence. Apparently, understanding an essence does not necessarily include understanding its being or existence. So there is a real distinction between essence, which answers the question "what is it?," and existence, which answers the question "is it?" Each one of us has a received existence. If existence were part of the "what" of us—that is, part of our essence—then we would necessarily exist. But we know that this is not the case. The act of existing is received. Each one of us came into existence.

Every finite being is composed of essence and existence, and "that which actualizes the essence is existence." Let us look at the following example to explain this further. The philosopher Aquinas *is* a rational animal, an essence. The horse Seabiscuit *is* an irrational animal, an essence. Whereas *esse* explains why these two beings are one (animal), *essence* is the reason why these two beings are not one. Therefore, *esse* is an inner component by which a living material being exists. And *essence* is an interior principle by which a living material being is what it is. Aquinas explains the oneness of beings by the fact that they all share the act of existence, which is itself one and the same simple act. But beings are different because this act of existence is received into many different essences.

To put it another way, essence is that which is signified by the definition of the thing. A kind of thing is then to be associated with an essence. The essence as what "makes something what it is" implies that this something is something, i.e., a particular kind of thing, such as a star, a number, a horse. It is called "essence" (*essentia*) because it is that through which and in which a thing has its being (*esse*). A being is that which is; it is something concrete; its essence is that thanks to which it is and is what it is.

Two other poles of metaphysics are being and change—or being and becoming, if you will. In our daily life we see things that are, and we see them change. As a consequence, what things will be is not completely manifest in what they presently are. Yet the question is how change can be reconciled with existence. If a thing changes, it is no longer what it was—so said Heraclitus. So for Heraclitus, all was change, constant flux. If a thing remains what it is, on the other hand, it cannot change—so said Parmenides. For Parmenides, being was preeminent. Aristotle found the happy medium between these extremes. A being may have existence in actuality, and a special kind of nonexistence called potency. Aquinas happily accepted this distinction—*act* and *potency.*

The doctrine of act and potency is a key element in Aquinas's philosophy. It describes, and more or less explains, how things have the capacity to change without losing their "identity." Perhaps a friendlier word for "potency" is potential: it is the capacity in a subject to become something that it is not. Water has the potential to become hot; a sitting person has the potential to run. If a subject cannot become or do or be something else, it lacks potency for it. Water cannot think; a horse cannot fly. We might also describe potency as a capacity for change in some way. Potency refers to that which is not actual—to what does not exist (yet). Air, for instance, is air, but can become fire. It has the actuality of air, but it also has the potentiality of becoming fire.

In the footsteps of Aristotle, Aquinas defines change as the transition from potentiality to actuality. All the things we experience undergo change because they are composed of actuality and potentiality, where change is just the actualization of a potential. Therefore, for Aquinas, motion or change is just the reduction of potency to act. So when we talk about one thing being moved by another, which in turn is moved by another, and so on—in a causal series of moves—then we just use shorthand for saying that a certain potency is reduced to act by something whose potency is itself reduced to act by something whose potency is itself reduced to act by... and so forth.

Another pivotal distinction for Aquinas is the one between substance and accidents. In general, we know each thing as a thing, as a *substance.* All things are composed of a substance—their primary mode of being. Therefore, the basis of reality lies in substances. However, substance is not an imaginative concept, but an abstract and rational concept. This means that we cannot picture what a substance is in our imagination; rather, we must use rationality, intellect, and logic to understand it. In addition to substance, all things have secondary modes of being called *accidents*. Accidents are those things that allow us to imagine a being or thing. Accidents are "attached" to an abstract substance and give it physicality. They can change without affecting the substance. So in Aquinas's metaphysics, substance does not mean what modern scientists mean when they use that term—a material body without regard to nature. A substance is something that exists in itself (being-in-self), not in another. In contrast, an accident is something that exists not in itself but in another—it cannot exist except in some substance (being-in-other). The hardest thing for the modern mind to grasp is that substance is per se immaterial—something real yet not composed of matter.

When Aquinas defines change as the transition from potentiality to actuality, he then distinguishes two different kinds of change: accidental change and substantial change. When a person gets older, wiser, or fatter, that is only a change in accidents, but when that person dies, that is a change in substance. Something remains the same in accidental changes, so I am still me even though all the cells of my entire body have died and been replaced by new cells. The "appearances" may change, but it remains the same substance. However, each person also goes through substantial change—actually twice, when we are conceived and when we die. To use another analogy, the monarch butterfly goes through dramatic changes from egg to caterpillar, to pupa, and finally to a mature butterfly, but through all this it remains a member of the species *Danaus plexippus*. So we have a case here of accidental changes—one and the same subject may go through various changes, but it remains the same entity. But when the butterfly dies, a substantial change is taking place, because that very event removes the subject itself of accidental changes.

As a side note: While it is possible for a substance to change its appearances through accidental changes without going through any substantial change, it is also possible for a substance to undergo a substantial change without losing its appearances. This phenomenon has become widely known as "transubstantiation."

To bring the above distinctions together, we could say that in the order of existence, *esse* is act and *essence* is potency. In the order of activity, *accident* is act, and *substance* is potency.

Matter and Form

Another pivotal distinction for Aquinas is the twosome matter and form. Each and every individual thing is composed not only of matter (*materia*) but also of form (*forma*). Matter is the possibility of form and has the potential for form. In the order of essence, form is act, and matter is potency. So form is the principle of determination that accounts for the thing being the kind of thing it is. As matter is the principle of potentiality—of the ability to become other than it is—form is the principle of actuality: of the thing being the sort of thing it actually is.

So the product of a change involves two things: matter and form. They cannot exist without each other. There are no beings without matter, and there are no beings without form. So the definition of a natural substance must contain both form and matter—otherwise it would be like a mathematical definition. Matter is the principle of individuality. G. K. Chesterton worded it well: "Matter is the more mysterious and indefinite and featureless element; and that what stamps anything with its own identity is its Form. Matter, so to speak, is not so much the solid as the liquid or gaseous thing in the cosmos; and in this most modern scientists are beginning to agree with him [Aquinas]. But the form is the fact; it is that which makes a brick a brick, and a bust a bust, and not the shapeless and trampled clay of which either may be made."

The distinction between matter and form allowed Aquinas in another way to make sense of the intriguing phenomenon of change: When X changes into Y, some part of X remains unchanged and some part of X alters. What endures is X's matter; what changes is X's form. This, then, allowed him to explain how something as simple as a chunk of marble could eventually become a statue. Its form was changed while its matter remained the same—so its potential to be a statue was actualized. The term "matter" pretty well corresponds in its use to some uses of the word "stuff" in modern English. When the stuff that Mary eats turns into Mary, Aquinas would say that the same matter was first food and then became part of a human body. "Matter" in itself cannot be known, since it always must show itself in a specific "form."

The concept of form may seem very elusive, but perhaps the following example may give it more "body." Fr. Joe Heschmeyer uses the example of isomers. When two or more (different) compounds share the same molecular formula, they are called isomers. For instance, there are three different compounds with the molecular formula C_3H_8O: methoxyethane, propanol, and rubbing alcohol. These are different substances, with different chemical properties. Yet these differences are not material, but formal. That is, each of the three substances is made up of identical atoms. It is the arrangement of those atoms that determines whether the substance will be methoxyethane, propanol, or rubbing alcohol. The same matter, with different forms, produces different substances.

A substance has an essence, and this will be expressed by the definition that tells us what it is, but the definition of a substance must include both matter and form. If a person is a substance composed of matter and form, this definition would not be matter plus form, or body plus soul, but rather "rational animal." It would be false to say that a person is matter, and it would also be false to say that a person is form. These are merely two inseparable constituents of what a person is. A body without a form, or soul, is a corpse; a soul without a body is what we call a spirit.

However, things can get a little more complicated. When a change of an object's form comes with a change in the object's substance, we call that (as discussed above) a *substantial* change, to distinguish it from accidental changes. For example, if a horse were to walk off a cliff and fall to its death, it would undergo both an accidental change (due to its change in posture and location) and a substantial change (caused by the death of the horse). We can no longer call the horse a living animal; instead, it has substantially changed into a carcass, and can no longer have the accidental changes it could go through before. A similar thing occurs in chemical reactions, to mention a modern example. If one admits that hydrogen and oxygen are different substances, and that they are each different from water, then one can see that the change from hydrogen and oxygen to water is a substantial change. What comes to be is a new form in the matter, i.e., in what persists through the change. This new form comes to be in what previously lacked that form. Thus, the form water comes to be in the matter of hydrogen and oxygen.

Correspondingly, as there is substantial change, there is also a principle of substantial form. The hydrogen that enters into a water molecule is no longer hydrogen when the molecule is a water molecule; rather, it is part of the substance of water. If this is the case, there must be a way in which hydrogen is "in" water, without water being hydrogen. If the substantial form of hydrogen were in water, then water would have two substantial forms, and would be given the same being by two different principles—which does not make sense.

In order to avoid this outcome, Aquinas recognizes the need both to maintain the substantial unity and primacy of the mixture, and to maintain the actual presence of the elements at the same time. He does so by introducing the concept of *virtuality*— or virtual presence. Do not confuse this term with the modern idea of "virtual" as describing something opposed to reality. Aquinas merely says that the elements are not actually in the substance, but they are there virtually, i.e., by their power (*virtus*). He does so to avoid the faulty idea that water would be simultaneously water, hydrogen, and oxygen, throughout the whole of the thing, when in fact it is water all the way through. There must be a way in which hydrogen is "in" water, but that water is not "hydrogen." Since there is no "middle way" between act and potency, the substantial forms of the elements are in some way in potency in the thing. This also accounts for the ability to produce elements from the mixture, since this ability remains. So the elemental substances are "virtually" present in the new combination.

As a side note, the so-called emergence theory (emergentism), which is becoming more and more popular nowadays in the so-called reductionism–holism debate, states that larger entities, patterns, and regularities arise through interactions among smaller or simpler entities that themselves do not exhibit such properties. However, this theory cannot explain the radical difference between the new substance and the elements it is composed of, except inasmuch as it describes *that* something comes about—the more complex by emerging from the more simple; but it does not explain *how*—as to how this new complexity comes about. Emergence cannot explain itself. But the concepts of substantial form and virtuality are able to provide the philosophical explanation for that complexity. The basis of the doctrine of virtual presence ultimately goes back to the dictum that something cannot come from nothing. The parts are only "virtually" in a substance, rather than "actually," and in a sense they depend on the whole as much as the whole depends on the parts.

To tie things together, the actuality/potentiality distinction implies that every finite substance is a compound of essence (potentiality) and existence (actuality), and that every material substance in particular is a compound of substantial form and prime matter—with substantial form corresponding to actuality and prime matter to potentiality. Form and matter make up a substantial unity; one cannot have form without matter, or matter without some form. But, although they are united, one can still distinguish these principles, and also understand that these principles are real features of the things that exhibit them. As a matter of fact, the concept of "form" is a universal principle presupposed by modern science, and thus modern science cannot disprove its existence—as we will soon see.

What Aquinas teaches us is that there must be something that is the basis of material things; we cannot define the nature of the material thing by simply subdividing the material into smaller and smaller particles. Stephen M. Barr uses the example of a liver and a muscle to explain that they "are made up of the same material constituents—hydrogen, carbon, oxygen, and so on—acting on each other by the same basic forces. It is precisely their forms, their organic structures, that differ and enable them to play different roles in the body."

Fivefold Causality

The natural sciences have as their object the world of changing things: from subatomic particles to cells to galaxies. Whenever there is a change there must be something that changes. The ancient Greeks are right: from nothing, nothing comes—that is, if the verb "to come" means to change. All change requires an underlying material reality—something has to change. But what is it that causes change? The principle of causality states that any potential, if actualized, must be actualized by something already actual. Following Aristotle, Aquinas distinguishes four causes of change, four kinds of causality: form and matter are the two intrinsic causes, namely the *formal* cause and the *material* cause; and the *efficient* and *final* causes are the two extrinsic causes. These four factors together answer why-questions about how things change and how natural processes "come about." Aquinas's point is that all four causes are necessary in order to capture the complexity of causal relations as they exist in the actual world.

Now the way Aristotle and Aquinas use the word "cause" can be confusing for modern readers who usually think of causes as efficient causes that literally cause something to change or to be. But Aristotle and Aquinas are referring to *four* different kinds of factors that explain how something changes. Each cause provides a different explanation—a different kind of answer to the question "why?" To fully grasp how Aristotle and Aquinas understood the four causes, you have to get inside their metaphysical systems. Allow me to settle for a common translation of these concepts into the modern vernacular: the *material* cause explains what something is made of; the *efficient* cause explains where something came from—who or what produced or moved it; the *formal* cause explains what something actually is; and the *final* cause explains the ultimate purpose toward which something tends. Aquinas usually specifies which kind of cause he has in mind; when he does not, he typically refers to the efficient cause.

To explain each type of cause we could use the following classic example that is dear to Aquinas. In response to the question "why is this house?," Aristotle and Aquinas distinguish four "whys": "what is it?" and "what is it made of?" and "who made it?" and "what is it for?" Hence, they give us four types of answers regarding why this is a house. The four answers are as follows: Because it is made of building material; because it is in the shape of a house; because a builder built it; because it is meant to be lived in. A description of each kind of cause is important for a full account of whatever a philosopher is trying to explain. I will clarify each type of cause separately.

All change requires an underlying material reality. In every change there is something that receives a new determination—this something is called the material cause (*causa materialis*). In our example, the wood or bricks are the material cause of a new house. A thing's material cause is the material of which it consists—a table is made of wood, a statue of marble. Before undergoing a change, it has the potential for a new determination, but in order to receive a new actualization, it needs the action of an efficient cause (more on this later).

Since each and every individual thing is composed not only of matter, but also of form, there needs to be a formal cause (*causa formalis*) as well, which accounts for the thing being the kind of thing it actually is. It is like the idea or blueprint of a thing. Whereas matter is the principle of potentiality, of the ability to become other than what a thing is, form is the principle of actuality, of the thing being the sort of thing it is. Aristotle and Aquinas speak of a formal cause to account for the reason why the material constituents are arranged in the way they are. In our example, the building material receives the shape or form of a house.

The formal cause explains why a substance exists as this particular kind of thing, while the material cause explains why it can cease to be what it is and become something else. In our example of building material receiving the form of a house, we have a case of *accidental* change, since what comes to be is a new accidental form (the shape) in what is already a certain substance (the bricks or wood). But there are also cases of *substantial* change—that is, cases of new substances coming to be. For example, when you eat an apple, the apple stops being an apple and becomes part of yourself.

Then there is a third type of cause. In order to receive a new actualization, the substance needs the action of an efficient cause (*causa efficiens*). In our example, the builder would be the efficient cause of the house—in the same way as parents are the efficient causes of their offspring. It is the cause that brings something about—the carpenter makes the table, the sculptor makes the statue, parents make children. The efficient cause is what we normally understand by the word cause, especially in science; it indicates something that has a certain effect.

Things change each other, make each other to be more or less, alter each other's existence. They exert genuine efficient causality on each other. But where does this remarkable ability come from? It comes from the fact that they exist. If something exists, it is in act, and it acts according to the kind of existence it has, and it impresses this existence on the things around it. The efficient cause of substantial changes are external to the thing that comes to be. The efficient cause of accidental changes can also be internal to the thing—for instance, when an animal moves, or an apple turns from green to red.

Lastly, there is a fourth type of cause. The final cause (*causa finalis*) is the full actualization of the form. It is what a thing is "for"—a knife is for cutting, a pump is for pumping. This concept has often received the charge of anthropomorphism, because it seems to imply that the pump has intentions as we do. However, for Aquinas, the fact that nature works "always or for the most part" to produce the same result is evidence that there is a genuine cause at work—a final cause, that is. The physical world displays a patterned consistency invariably directed toward specified ends, thereby making prediction possible. It reflects the generally accepted idea in science that "like causes have like effects." When scientists talk about cause-and-effect relationships, Aquinas would say they are speaking in terms of both *causa efficiens* and *causa finalis*. Aquinas actually called the final cause the "cause of causes," by which he meant to call attention to the fact that it is the final cause that lends intelligibility to the three other causes.

What Aristotle and Aquinas call a "final cause" has fallen out of modern usage, possibly because it's not considered scientific. However, a final cause should not necessarily be understood as a "purpose" in the sense of a "reason for," but as an "end" in the sense of having built-in ways of behaving. All things act in definite ways. Puppies become dogs but they never become horses, and rocks cannot swim and never will. This is final causality—it causes things to be directed to their specific ends. In the words of William E. Carroll, "If there were no end-directed or end-seeking behavior in physical reality, there would be no regularities, functions, or structures about which we could formulate laws of nature and make predictions." Any ordering of efficient causes and their effects implicitly acknowledges and presupposes that the efficient causes and the processes that embody them are directed toward the realization of certain specific types of outcomes. Efficient causes always have certain specifiable results—their *effects*. The notion of final causality is inherently connected with the concept of potentiality. In the words of Aristotle, if "the end of an acorn is to be a tree, in some way the acorn is only potentially a tree but not actually so at this time." Therefore, by realizing its final cause, the acorn becomes an oak tree by actualizing its potential.

Final causes may be anathema for some scientists, but for Aquinas, there is no way to make sense of the fact that an efficient cause X always generates a certain specific effect or range of effects Y—rather than Z, or no effect at all—if we don't suppose that X inherently "points to" or is "directed at" Y as toward an end or goal. All efficient causes are goal-directed or effect-oriented, so to speak. Efficient causal power goes hand in hand with finality or directedness; deny the latter and you implicitly deny the former. If there is no finality inherent in nature, then there are no real potencies in nature either, for a potency is always a potency for some particular outcome, toward which it "points" or is directed. To deny finality in nature would be implicitly to deny that natural substances have real causal power and that there is any real potency in nature—which would actually undermine the foundations of natural science. Some still think we should dismiss final causes because Aristotle's view that heavy objects are naturally directed toward the center of the earth as their "natural place" turned out to be mistaken. This is often treated as a reason for rejecting the idea of final causality, but this simply does not follow. The effect of gravity is final causality, namely, that things fall toward the earth. When interpreted properly, the idea of final causality makes perfect sense.

What Aquinas added to these four Aristotelian causes is the exemplary cause (*causa exemplaris*). Exemplary causality is defined as "the causal influence exercised by a model or an exemplar . . . on the operation of an agent." To use our example of a house again, the builder must already have in mind the house he wants to create in order for him to be able to do just that, and in order for there to be a house in the end: "Before something begins to be in reality, it is already in the mind of the agent," says Aquinas. This blueprint in the mind of the builder is an example of an exemplary cause. Thus, the idea or plan that a man working on a project has in mind can be an exemplary cause in relation to that project. And this would also apply to God, in Aquinas's view: God would be considered the exemplary cause of all creation. We must keep in mind here that Aquinas's philosophy cannot be understood without his theology. The exemplary cause is "a form or idea in imitation of which something comes to be." These are the "ideas" in the mind of God.

All these distinctions may seem nitpicky at first glance, but they are very rich and powerful. They can help us understand new scientific developments better, as the upcoming chapters will, I hope, demonstrate. Making distinctions may seem burdensome, but as the philosopher Jacques Maritain observed, we must "distinguish in order to unite." Aquinas offers us a rich concept of causality: efficient causes presuppose final causes, and final causes are in turn essentially connected to substantial forms, and thus to formal causes, which in turn are instantiated in matter, and thus require material causes. Unfortunately, as the Scientific Revolution exerted its influence on the philosophical world in the seventeenth century, causality was reduced from Aquinas's five causes to one single cause, namely, the efficient cause. The term "cause" became synonymous with "event preceding an effect," and the classical meaning of cause as a form of "explanation" was basically eliminated. Hence, notions such as final and formal cause gradually dropped out of consideration, since they could not be represented in a mathematical way.

Primary and Secondary Cause

Aristotle had stated that God is the "first cause" of all causes, but Aquinas changed this drastically. He took God out of this sequence of causes and placed God not at its beginning but "above" and "beyond" the sequence of regular causes. He calls God a "primary cause," and all the causes that nature and the natural sciences deal with he considered "secondary causes." The physical causality of nature, as studied in science, reigns "inside" the universe, linking causes together in a chain of secondary causes. God, on the other hand, reigns from "outside" the universe as a primary cause or first cause, thus providing some sort of "point of suspension" for the chain of secondary causes. A thing can cause *other* things to change, but it cannot be the cause of its *own* existence. Therefore, says Aquinas, God is the "first *exemplar* cause of all things." What is so special about the primary cause is that it needs *no* cause. And what is so special about secondary causes is that they *do* need a cause.

Perhaps we need some more clarification here regarding the distinction between a primary cause and all the causes that science deals with, namely, the secondary causes. It is the secondary causes that we are all familiar with—"like causes having like effects." Science deals with this kind of causality. It is the causality that reigns "inside" the universe, linking causes together in a chain of secondary causes—the chains of causes and effects, for instance, that cosmologists usually talk about. How can we explain this chain of causes? Circular causation is obviously out of the question—in the simple, straightforward words of the philosopher Michael Augros, "You can't be your own father." Infinite regression won't work either. True, a sequence of events in time may be able to go infinitely forward through the future and back through the past, but the problem would be that time itself must have some other form of cause. Besides, any part of the chain can only do any causing if it first exists. In other words, the need for causes must come to an end: there must be or have been a cause that is not itself in need of a cause—a primary cause. Things caused by something else cannot be self-explanatory.

This is the point where the logical need for a primary cause comes in; as stated above, it provides a point of suspension for the chain of secondary causes. Augros uses the simple example of an I-beam with a hook on it from which a chain is to be hung: "If there is nothing for that whole chain to hang from, it will not hang, and nothing can be hung from it. There is nothing about those links in themselves that makes them want to hang in space. . . . There must also be something *from* which things hang and which is not itself hanging from anything." Whether this primary cause is identical to God is another question. The two terms are not synonyms, but they may turn out to be referring to the same entity. However, it could easily be argued, but not here, that the first cause cannot be other than God. He is the Eternal and Infinite, "in whom we live and move and have our being" (Acts 17:28).

Some may wonder what caused the first cause, or who created the Creator. The idea behind this question is that "everything needs a cause," but that statement would lead to an infinite regression. Instead we should rephrase the question as follows: "Everything that has come into existence needs a cause." Something that does not exist cannot bring itself into existence. But the primary cause never came into existence—which means God is the uncaused cause, the eternal cause who has always been in existence. Therefore, the question "who created God?" is illogical, just like "to whom is the bachelor married?" Secondary causes are contingent; that is to say, they don't have to exist, and thus because they do exist, we can ask for the cause of their existence. God, on the other hand, is a necessary and eternal being who did not come into existence but always has been. Since God transcends the world of cause and effect, God is not determined by the world of cause and effect.

When Aquinas developed the distinction between primary and secondary causality, he tapped into core Christian ideas of God and God's creation. God's being is self-sufficient, is the fountain of the being of all that exists, and does not depend on anything outside of God. From a *rational* point of view, there must be some power transcending this world, some infinite, eternal, absolute, and uncaused power—typically called God or Creator. The Creator is uncaused and yet is the "cause" or "ground" of all other, secondary, causes. God is the ultimate cause of all being;

God is the beginning and the end of all that exists. Creatures have their own existence, but they nevertheless require the divine founding action that enables their existence and activity. Since existence is not part of the essence of things, it needs to be explained by a cause extrinsic to the thing that exists—an uncaused cause.

How are we to understand this? I borrow here some great thoughts, and even sentences, from William E. Carroll, a historian of science at Oxford University (see the reference at the end of this chapter). It is important to emphasize that, unlike secondary causes, the primary cause is unique. It is not the first of a series of causes all belonging to the same level. It is very tempting to think along these lines: the first cause, God, creates a human being; this human being is the second cause, who hires an architect; this architect is the third cause, who instructs a builder; and so forth. But this is certainly not what Aquinas meant. The chain of causes needs somehow a suspension point, so to speak. When Aquinas describes God as the first cause, what he means is not merely "first" in the sense of being before the second cause in time, and not "first" in the sense of coming before the second cause in a sequence, but rather "first" in the sense of being the *source* of all secondary causes, having absolutely primal and underived causal power—a power from which all other causes derive their causal powers. As Edward Feser puts it, "secondary causes" are not "second" in the sense of coming after the first and before the third member of the series, but rather in the sense of having their causal power only in a secondary or derivative way. In other words, when Aquinas speaks of a "first" cause, his concern is logical hierarchy rather than temporal priority. God is not an originating, preceding cause in the past but a fundamental cause in the present. Michael Augros explains the difference as follows:

> First cause is a bit like the expression first prize. First prize does not usually mean the prize awarded first in time. In contests, third prize is often awarded first, second prize next, first prize last, to build excitement and avoid anticlimax. First prize means instead a prize that ranks before all

other prizes in value or significance. Similarly, the great thinkers who all insist there is a first cause used the expression first cause not to mean (necessarily) a cause before all other causes in time, but a cause before all others in causal power. It meant a cause of other causes that does not itself depend on any other cause. It meant, in other words, something that exists and acts all by itself, without deriving its existence or causal action from anything else. And it meant not a thing stuck in the past, but a thing existing in the present.

What Aquinas does in all of this is safeguard God's *transcendence*. Thanks to this concept, God is not a deity like Jupiter—not a being stronger than other beings and superior to all other beings, yet acting like all other beings. Instead, God is the very source of all being—the absolute ground of all that happens to exist. This primary cause is uncaused, not even self-caused, but the source of all being; not some superbeing among other beings, who acts like other beings, but an absolute being; not a cause prior to and larger than other causes, but a primary cause; not a power stronger than and superior to all other powers, but an infinite power; not a supercause among other causes, but a power "above" and "beyond" all secondary causes. When the transcendence of the first cause is overlooked, its influence on secondary causes becomes either an enigma or a contradiction. God is not a rival or contender for created causes, but rather the One who makes all secondary causes be causes.

The other side of the coin is that God not only respects the activity of creatures, God also allows and guarantees their own activity. It is only thanks to the primary cause that creatures can become secondary causes and act like causes. Although God keeps things and their causal powers in being, these also bring about their own effects all by themselves. Aquinas explains that the way God's providence works is through a hierarchy of causes. God, the universal or primary cause of all creation, ordained that the universe would be governed by a series of secondary causes. Interestingly enough, it was Isaac Newton's belief that the universal law of gravity could not otherwise be explained but by assuming a Lawgiver.

In a sense, God is all-present in all secondary causes. One simple example of this is that God made a universe in which objects attract each other, a phenomenon that we call the force of gravity. This force is a secondary cause. By allowing such inferior causes to operate, God made a universe in which He does not have to be the direct cause of every stone falling to the ground. It is through His laws of nature that the all-powerful God is all-present. Therefore, we are able to know what the outcome is of certain contingent events like trees falling. We do not have to wonder about God's will every time a tree falls to the ground, even if it strikes us on the head when it does. God has given us a secondary cause—the force of gravity—which is the direct cause of each tree's earthly plummet.

Aquinas would say that these laws of nature are built into the very things themselves. Things have distinctive natures or forms that act in distinctive ways. The laws of nature, then, are not primarily abstract principles, or formulas, that are applied to each electron, for instance, in order to give it certain properties, but rather, each electron has a distinctive nature and action from which we abstract the laws about it. In Aquinas's view, as Edward Feser explains, a "law of nature" is a description of how things will tend to operate given their natures, essences, or substantial forms. The existence and operation of laws of nature thus presupposes the existence and operation of concrete natural substances. The laws are not even formal causes but rather mere descriptions of how things operate given their formal causes, i.e., their substantial forms. "Laws," in his view, are just abstractions from a concrete physical reality that behaves in accordance with the laws from which this concrete physical reality itself comes.

Because of this, God does not compete with any creature, not even our parents. Our parents are the natural cause of our being here—a secondary cause, that is—but God remains the transcendent primary cause of our being in existence and alive. That is why we could say that children come through us but not from us. Even if we have children, they are not "our own"; they come ultimately from God, the source and ground of all that exists—otherwise they could not even exist, nor could we. To put it in a catchphrase, God is "part" of everything in this universe, but without being a physical "part" of it. God is the first cause who operates in and through secondary causes.

It is hopefully clear by now that Aquinas's insight is vital for understanding the relationship between science and religion. The empirical sciences study the nature and activity of secondary causes, but metaphysics and theology study God's providence and divine action in creation. These two perspectives are different and complementary, but are certainly not opposed to each other (see chapter 2). Aquinas would say that the natural sciences are fully competent to account for the changes that occur in the natural world. The assumption that secondary causes are true causes, even if ultimately dependent on God, is necessary if natural science is to be possible—otherwise there would be no natural regularities to discover. To know what the natural world is like, we need both the empirical sciences and a philosophy of nature. It could be argued that a tendency toward a different conception of divine causality is part of what distinguishes Christianity from other religions—which might explain why natural science improved in the West and never really developed in the rest of the world (see chapter 5).

In Aquinas's conception, God causes creatures to exist in such a way that they are the real causes of their own operations. But it is important to recognize that divine causality (primary cause) and creaturely causality (secondary causes) function at fundamentally different levels. Yet, they are closely connected. In his *Summa contra Gentiles*, Aquinas remarks that "the same effect is not attributed to a natural cause and to divine power in such a way that it is partly done by God, and partly by the natural agent; rather, it is wholly done by both." As a consequence, any created effect comes, on the one hand, totally and immediately from God as the transcendent primary cause and, on the other hand, totally and immediately from the creature as secondary cause.

The question that remains, of course, is how metaphysics could ever use reason to reach into heaven, where God resides. Aquinas's answer is twofold. Reason alone can never reach God in His very own being—only faith can. The other part of the answer is that faith is consistent with reason, so it can never be unreasonable or irrational, since all truths are harmonious with one another. It is especially from this latter viewpoint that Aquinas formulated his five arguments for the existence of God. He called them actually "Five Ways" (the *Quinque Viae* in his *Summa Theologiae*).

Here are his five arguments in a nutshell. In the Argument from Motion, Aquinas argues that since everything that moves is moved by another, there must therefore exist an Unmoved Mover. In the Argument from Efficient Cause, he argues that the sequence of causes that make up this universe must have a First Cause. In the Argument from Contingency, he argues that since all existent things depend upon other things for their existence, there must exist at least one thing that is not dependent, and therefore is a Necessary Being. In the Argument from Gradation, he argues that since all existent things have different degrees of goodness, there must exist something that is an Absolutely Good Being. In the Argument from Design, also known as the Teleological Argument, he argues that the intricate design and order of existent things and natural processes imply that a Great Designer exists.

Let us start with the Argument from Contingency as an example, because the four other Ways Aquinas mentions could be taken as variations on this one particular Way. The point of departure is that our universe need not be the way it is, and it need not even exist. We are *contingent* beings who could easily not have existed, as the reason for our existence cannot be found within ourselves, so we depend for our existence on an overarching, transcending "ground"—a first cause or primary cause, a necessary being, or an absolute ground, if you will. Existence is something received. However, if there is no inherent necessity for the universe to exist, then the universe is not self-explanatory and therefore must find an explanation outside itself. Obviously, it cannot be grounded in something else that is also finite and not self-explanatory—that would lead to infinite regress—so it can only derive from an unconditioned, infinite, and ultimate ground, which is a Creator God—a being not self-caused but uncaused.

It is not very likely that Aquinas really thinks one can demonstrate or prove the existence of God with the Five Ways. It is rather telling that he does not call them "Five Proofs" but "Five Ways." He does not end each Way with QED (*quod erat demonstrandum*), but with the statement, "And this all think of as God." This takes us back to Aquinas's saying: "We must believe that God exists, which is clear by reason." What Aquinas means by this statement is that *reason* leads us to assume a primary cause, whereas *faith* in God discovers that this very concept refers to the God of our faith. This does not mean that reason can fully fathom God, for elsewhere he says, "We cannot understand what God is, but what He is not." In other words, our philosophical knowledge is limited to knowing *that* God is, more so than what or who He is. Yet, reason tells us that this universe cannot explain itself, but rather needs an ultimate non-contingent explanation. So these Ways are more like insights than proofs. We should not forget what Thomas Aquinas remarked: "To one who has faith, no explanation is necessary. To one without faith, no explanation is possible."

The late philosopher Ralph McInerny points out that Aquinas is very aware of the difference between "God" used as a proper noun and "god" used as a common noun. The ambiguity is pronounced in Latin, which lacks the indefinite article "a," whereas in English we can differentiate between "God" and "a god." The situation is worsened by translations that simply translate *deus* in the Five Ways as "God" in English. In the Five Ways, Aquinas does not use "god" as a proper name, but as a common noun having five different definitions. So each of the Ways concludes that there is "*a* god." Thus, it is also true that the Five Ways do not as such prove that there is only one god. It is for this reason that Aquinas himself thinks one must actually argue additionally that a god must be utterly unique, and thus that there can be only one, which he does in several questions after the Five Ways. Of course, once the utter uniqueness of "a god" has been shown, one can begin to use "God" as a proper name to refer to that one, utterly unique being, as he subsequently does in his *Summa Theologiae*.

It is not surprising that there is much disagreement among Thomists regarding how to interpret the Five Ways. Let me just say this. Although the Five Ways of Aquinas may not be taken as conclusive proofs of God's existence in a logical or mathematical sense, they could still be accepted in a *rational* sense: they offer strong reasons or arguments for God's existence, which makes them work as powerful pointers to a Creator God as the best possible—and arguably only—rational explanation for the fact that this universe does exist and is the way it is. The physicist and Anglican priest John Polkinghorne calls them "pointers to the divine as the only totally adequate ground of intelligibility." The fact that there is any world at all, or any causality at all, or any law at all, is the proper starting point of an argument for God as primary cause. Clouds, trees, plants, animals, human beings, societies, buildings, planets, and stars certainly exist, but they don't have to exist. Aquinas saw very clearly that their being is not self-explanatory, but depends, finally, on some primordial reality that does exist through the power of its own essence. This "necessary" being is what Aquinas called "a god," and identified eventually as "God."

Let us wrap up this discussion. Whatever exists is caused to be by God; this is a conclusion in metaphysics. Whether human souls are among the things that exist is a question to be answered in natural philosophy (see chapter 10); whether human beings are made in God's image is a theological issue; whether living things have evolved by natural selection is the subject of evolutionary biology (see chapter 9).

To open the mind for further study:

Augros, Michael. *Who Designed the Designer? A Rediscovered Path to God's Existence*. San Francisco, CA: Ignatius Press, 2015.

Carroll, William E. *Creation and Science*. London: CTS Books, 2011.

Owens, Joseph. *An Elementary Christian Metaphysics*. Houston, TX: Center for Thomistic Studies, 1985.

Wippel, John F. *The Metaphysical Thought of Thomas Aquinas: From Finite Being to Uncreated Being*. CUA Press, 2000.

4

Aquinas and Epistemology

EPISTEMOLOGY is the branch of philosophy concerned with the nature and scope of human knowledge. It studies what knowledge is and how it can be acquired. It is here that Aquinas offers us some very solid foundations and sound considerations. Although his terminology may be seen as complex, his message is basically simple and a lifesaver for scientific knowledge. Why is it, we should ask first, that Aquinas's epistemology is so greatly needed?

Epistemology in Crisis

The recent collapse of logical empiricism and the rise of historicism and social constructivism in the philosophy of science have basically left all of the sciences without any epistemology. For many of us, the only alternatives left are probabilism, pragmatism, and relativism—except for a few lonely voices calling out from the desert. It is here that Aquinas comes to our rescue.

Why is epistemology so much in disarray nowadays? It is a long history of detrimental developments, running from René Descartes (1596–1650), to John Locke (1632–1704), to George Berkeley (1685–1753), to David Hume (1711–1776), and to Immanuel Kant (1724–1804). It more or less started with Descartes's split between *res extensa* and *res cogitans*, with the former denuding the world of sensible qualities and the latter creating the impression that all such qualities—and the nature that underlies them, *"das Ding an sich"*—are projected into the universe by the observer. This has led to what Alfred North Whitehead called "bifurcation," which affirms that reality divides into an "external" world, consisting of things that can be described in mathematical terms, and an "internal" world of the thinker or observer. Owing to philosophers like these, many of us have ended up as Kantians, not knowing things in themselves, indeed not knowing that there are things at all. Following such ideas, many modern philosophers tend to think of our rational minds imposing meaning on the world. Giving priority to mere ideas in our coming to know external things easily generates both Hume's skepticism as to whether we can know the external world at all and Berkeley's claim that "to be is to be perceived" (*esse est percipi*). How are we supposed to know if this "external" world, which no human eye can ever behold, does in fact exist?

Probably the main troublemaker in this process was the philosopher David Hume. Not only did Hume strip our understanding of efficient causality and of final causality, he even called into question the narrow idea of efficient causality itself. In order to do so, he used the famous example of a billiard ball moving in a straight line toward another. There are several possibilities: the first ball bounces back with the second ball remaining at rest, or the first ball stops and the second ball moves, or the first ball jumps over the second, and so on. There is no reason to favor any of these possibilities over the others. Only through previous observation can one predict what will actually happen with the balls. All we observe is that the motion of the first billiard ball is followed by the motion of the second billiard ball—but the act of causation we cannot observe. Nor does the mind perceive the workings of cause and effect—otherwise we could determine what effects would follow from causes without ever having to rely on observation. Furthermore, we do not actually experience the necessary connection itself—we only infer it from the constant conjunction that we observe between two events. That's Hume's account in a nutshell.

It is not surprising that Hume used this particular example, because at the time the billiard-ball model had become standard in explaining the nature of the universe. In addition, the billiard-ball model stood for a kind of causal action that was thought to be evident, because the mechanism of this kind of action was supposedly clear and all-pervading. It was an example of "impulse," that is, of one body causing changes in another body by means of contact—by pushing it or striking it. "Impulse," John Locke once wrote, is "the only way which we can conceive Bodies operate in." What Hume did, in contrast, is argue that this "mechanism" was really a kind of illusion produced by habit or custom. All such cases are supposedly nothing but constant conjunctions, and our perceptions of them never give us insight into the modus operandi of the connection. Causal connections, in his view, turned out to be mere "metaphysical" inventions, based on an illusion.

Since the supposed influence of a cause upon its effect was not directly evident to sense observation, Hume concluded that the connection between cause and effect was not an aspect of the real world, but only a habit of our thinking as we become accustomed to see one thing constantly conjoined to another. Causality was thus reduced to correlation at most—a property not of things but of thoughts. It was no longer an ontological reality in the world outside ourselves, but an epistemological property of the way we *think* about the world. We simply imagine causality. In his own words, "From causes which appear similar we *expect* similar effects."

This stand made Hume one of the first skeptic philosophers to question the very idea of causality—actually of objective truth in general. Hume was right, we do not see causation in the same way in which we see colors and shapes and motion. But that does not mean we don't *experience* causation at all. To reduce causation to a habitual connection in the mind does not do justice to our actual experience. When I hear the cock crow before dawn every morning, it never occurs to me that the cock's crowing is causing the sun to rise. Apparently, we do not equate causation with correlation. That's why we always question correlations as to whether they are based on causal relations. Once we follow Hume and give up this distinction, we are in deep trouble.

The end result is a destructive form of skepticism. Skeptics like Hume find a flaw in every truth claimed, including the truth of causality—they are "masters of suspicion." Why argue anyway, if truth does not matter? Skepticism makes for a very restrained view of the world—actually so restrained that absolute skeptics cannot even know whether they have a mind to doubt with.

Skeptics turn things the wrong way. Granted we often do need to eliminate errors to get to the truth, yet our ultimate goal is not to avoid errors, but to gain truth—to know rather than to know what we do not know. Skeptics, on the other hand, make it their final goal to avoid errors, in denial of the fact that eliminating errors is only a means to gaining truth about reality. Once we begin questioning the trustworthiness of our brains and senses and reason, there is no way of establishing their trustworthiness again independently of trusting them.

Concerning the question of whether we can prove that the primary act of recognition of any reality is real, G.K. Chesterton saw clearly that Aquinas "recognised instantly, what so many modern sceptics have begun to suspect rather laboriously; that a man must either answer that question in the affirmative, or else never answer any question, never ask any question, never even exist intellectually, to answer or to ask." And then he adds, "Most fundamental sceptics appear to survive, because they are not consistently skeptical and not at all fundamental. They will first deny everything and then admit something, if for the sake of argument or often rather of attack without argument."

Once we accept Hume's conclusions to be true, the very foundation of all the sciences begins to crumble. Hence it should not surprise us that Hume's view is certainly not embraced by great physicists such as Max Planck and Albert Einstein, who both believed that physical laws describe a reality independent of ourselves, and that the theories of science show not only how nature behaves but why it behaves exactly as it does and not otherwise. Most scientists would in fact agree with them—although not always openly and happily. Besides, Hume's analysis would erase the important scientific distinction between causality and correlation; they would both be reduced to a series of mere subjective associations or generalizations. In contrast, scientists always want to make sure that causality is not just a matter of correlation; there certainly is, for instance, a correlation between wind velocity and windmill activity, but it is only the wind that causes windmill activity, not the other way around.

In spite of contrary claims made by David Hume and his followers, most people agree and accept that we do have knowledge of an external world beyond our mental habits. When we see the sun rise every morning, we know, for instance, that there is not a different sun rising every morning. The problem with a claim like "there is no such thing as objective truth" is that it claims to be objectively true. We cannot assert anything without also asserting, implicitly, that there is such a thing as objective truth after all. Claiming objective truth is not an empirical statement, based on a growing collection of evidence, but rather it is one of those universal truths that philosophy analyzes. It is a universal principle that convinces us of its truth independently of any particular cases that help us to establish it. Its truth does not increase when we see more examples of such statements. It is a universal principle.

We intuitively know there is a way things *are*, independent of how they may be apprehended. Any other view would undermine science. Although we know the world through sensations or sense impressions, they are just the media that give us access to reality. The Scottish philosopher John Haldane put it well when he said, "One only knows about cats and dogs through sensations, but they are not themselves sensations, any more than the players in a televised football game are color patterns on a flat screen." Knowledge does rest on sensation, but that doesn't mean it is confined to it. It is "reality" that forces us sometimes to revise our theories. But if we were to follow Hume's philosophy, we would end up with what the late physicist and historian of science Stanley Jaki calls "bricks without mortar." Jaki says about Hume's sensations, "The bricks he used for construction were sensory impressions. Merely stacking bricks together never produces an edifice, let alone an edifice that is supposed to be the reasoned edifice of knowledge." In other words, we need a different epistemology—one that does not treat something like the "law of causality" as a general statement that requires more and more cases to become validated in an inductive way, but rather as a universal principle that is true independently of any particular cases. It is Aquinas who offers us this remedy. In the words of Stanley Jaki, "For Aquinas it is natural for man to be in a cognitive unity with nature."

Epistemology Restored

Curiously enough, Hume rejects metaphysical entities on metaphysical grounds. Hume's metaphysical assumption is that cause and effect are not rooted in the identity of acting *things*, but in a relationship between *events*. In taking this road, Hume and his followers have left us in a cognitive desert. So perhaps another kind of metaphysics can bring us back to reality. Scientists sometimes joke about their work with warnings like, "Don't touch anything in a physics lab," or, "Don't taste anything in a chemistry lab," or, "Don't smell anything in a biology lab." But perhaps we should add here, "Don't buy anything in a philosophy department."

How could Aquinas's philosophy help us reverse such fatal developments—fatal for common sense, but even more so for science? How can Aquinas possibly bring the so greatly needed realism and objectivity back to human knowledge? Albert Einstein once begged for this: "The belief in an external world independent of the perceiving subject is the basis of all natural science." Interestingly enough, Aquinas's philosophy has sometimes been described as a philosophy of common sense. Chesterton even put it this way: "The fact that Thomism is the philosophy of common sense is itself a matter of common sense." And then he adds, "To this question 'Is there anything?' St. Thomas begins by answering 'Yes'; if he began by answering 'No', it would not be the beginning, but the end."

From the perspective of Aquinas, the philosophical approach advocated by Hume and his followers looks awfully contrived and artificial; instead of focusing on human beings actively engaged with things in the world, it offers us an abstract mind trying desperately to find entry into the world by connecting events. Sometimes a seemingly logical analysis leads to a conclusion that cannot possibly be true. Take the case of a pie that gets cut in half each time new visitors come in. The cutting in half can be done into infinity. Although the pieces get smaller and smaller each time, we seem to have an endless pie. That sounds very compelling, but everyone knows intuitively this cannot be true. It may not be easy to determine where the error is located, but we do know there must be an error somewhere. The same seems to be the case with Hume's analysis—we know it can't be true.

So what is wrong with Hume's analysis, from Aquinas's perspective? Notice what is being affirmed here—that something metaphysical such as "causal connections" depends on what the imagination creates. Hume came to this view because he took causality as a relationship of *events*, assuming that "all events seem entirely loose and separate" and that "we can never observe any tie between them." As a consequence, causal connections in themselves ultimately became subjective phenomena in Hume's view.

How different is this view of causality from Aquinas's view. He considers cause and effect to be rooted in the identity of acting things. What a thing *is*, says Aquinas, will determine what it *does*. An acorn can become an oak tree, and not a butterfly, because that is its nature. The actions an entity can take are determined by what that entity is. According to this latter view, when one billiard ball strikes another, it sends it rolling because of the nature of the balls and their surroundings—and not just antecedent events. The philosopher James Hill explains what this entails: When we know that billiard balls are solid and when we see one ball moving toward another, then certain effects are quite impossible. The moving ball cannot, for example, just pass through the second ball and come out the other side continuing at the same speed; nor can the first ball stop at exactly the same place as the second ball; nor can one of the balls suddenly vanish, and so on and so forth. The qualities of the balls determine the kind of effect that the impulse of the first ball will have on the second.

Moreover, the law of causality is an objective given. Contrary to Hume's notion that causal connections ultimately depend on the input of human imagination, causality seen as a relationship between an entity and its own actions exists independently of our consciousness. When we see entities acting, we see causality. In Hume's view, in contrast, the law of a daily sunrise is not "out there" but is merely a mental conception based on our habit of seeing the sun rise every morning. The late philosopher Joseph Bochenski questions this view seriously: If laws of nature were just mental habits, it would be hard to explain why bridges built in accordance with the proper physical laws and boundary conditions stand firm whereas others collapse. Do competent engineers really have better mental habits than their inept colleagues? There has got to be more to it! G. K. Chesterton once "seriously joked" about a conspiracy of order in our world of regularity: "One elephant having a trunk was odd, but all elephants having trunks looked like a plot." Well, science is in search of that plot!

How can we search for that plot? Aquinas agrees with Aristotle that "nothing is in the intellect that is not first in the senses." What he meant is that what is immediately sensed—"qualities" or "impressions" in Hume's terminology, such as colors, sounds, and odors—are only the media through which reality is discerned and understood; we are not confined to those sensations. Yet the starting point of all knowledge is that we absorb knowledge first through our senses. To put the basis of his epistemology in a nutshell: to know is to know things, not to know mental abstractions. We have to distinguish between abstractions and the concrete objects that instantiate the abstractions. Knowledge is about reality, not about knowledge. Either we conform our minds to reality, or we shape reality to conform to our thinking. Aquinas tells us that we must choose the former, not the latter. Contrary to what Hume claims, we are dealing here with truth and reason, not sentiment and habit. G. K. Chesterton once firmly asserted "that truth exists whether we like it or not, and that it is for us to accommodate ourselves to it."

What is fundamental for Aquinas is that all knowledge is based on the senses. The senses provide the material that the intellect processes. In his own words, "Our knowledge, taking its start from things, proceeds in this order. First, it begins in the senses; second, it is completed in the intellect." For Aquinas, the senses are only the starting point of knowledge. Sense experience begins in the *senses*, but it is completed in the *intellect*. What this means is that we must learn what it is to perceive the world as it presents itself in sense experience. The apple is outside us, but we perceive it nonetheless, with its colors and its other attributes, which are as real as we sense them to be. The apple is not inside of us. Later, the philosopher Edmund Husserl would say that knowledge is not like a box, allowing things to be only inside or outside the box. He considered it best to compare knowledge to a source of light; if a light beam hits a certain thing that is in darkness, this thing will be in the light, and yet it won't be inside the source of light—the mind, that is.

What Aquinas tells us here is actually a state-of-the-art view. Nowadays, we know how incomplete the information is that comes from the senses; sensorial data must be "processed" first before they can become information. Optical illusions show us how ambiguous the image on the retina can be. Even depth perception requires a great deal of mental processing. Or consider a statue that looks so different from different angles, yet we know it is the same statue—a phenomenon called "constancy." Although the images keep changing on the retina, we perceive constancy. Apparently, changing images do not necessarily give rise to changing perceptions. The experimental psychologist Irvin Rock once put it in these concise terms: "The usefulness of the analogy of the eye to a camera ends with the formation of that image; the problem of perception then begins. . . . Given the similarity of the eye to a camera, the mystery of our perception is how we manage to transcend the inadequate, distortion-prone, ambiguous, two-dimensional images established on the retina and achieve the rich, constant, usually correct, three-dimensional representation of the world that we do." This becomes even more of a mystery when we consider the more intellectual part of perception—cognition. A stick, for instance, appears bent when part of it is outside the water, yet we know it is straight.

Obviously, human knowledge is more than a collection of sense data. For Aquinas, sense experience provides only the "passive" component of knowledge; in addition, there is the *intellect*, which provides the active component of knowledge. Whereas the eye only sees, without seeing that it sees, the intellect knows, but also knows that it knows. Obviously, intellectual knowledge surpasses sensorial knowledge. Like a camera, the eye registers whatever light is there for it to register, but knowledge goes beyond this information. The intellect depends on sense data, but it changes images into perception, and then perception into cognition, by using concepts and reasoning, thus making sensorial experiences *intelligible* for the human mind.

This is a one-way process—from sense data to perception to cognition—so cognition does not change perception, nor does perception change the sense data. All we know about the world does come through our physical senses but is then processed by the immaterial intellect, which extracts from sensory experiences that which is intelligible with the aid of concepts (Aquinas uses the term *species*). Concepts are not things but, according to Aquinas, the "informed activity of the intellect as it grasps the thing." As a matter of fact, the Latin term *conceptum* can have our meaning of "concept" but can also mean "thing conceived." The latter is more in accord with Aquinas's use.

A concept may be as simple as a "circle" or as complex as a "gene," but a concept definitely goes beyond what the senses provide. Concepts are not perceived pictures or images. Pictures are by nature ambiguous, open to various interpretations; so we would still need concepts to interpret them. We do not "see" genes but have come to hypothesize them and conceptualize them. We do not even see circles, for a "circle" is a highly abstract, idealized concept (with a radius, diameter, and circumference). It is through mental concepts that we can transform "things" of the world into "objects" of knowledge; they change experiences into observations, thus enabling us to see with our "mental eyes" what no physical eyes could ever see. We do not understand genetics, for instance, without a concept such as "gene."

Aquinas gives us quite an intricate analysis of the process that leads from senses to intellect. He basically distinguishes passive sensation from active perception. He speaks actually about a three-step process. When we perceive an object—through the process of *sensation*—our mind composes a sense image, which resembles what became known as "sense data" in some recent philosophical traditions. Aquinas likens sensation to wax being impressed with the shape of a seal. The step after sensation is *imagination*. During this second step, we are imagining the form and structure of what we recollect from sensation. This creates what Aquinas calls a "phantasm" (*phantasma*). When we then extract information from this phantasm, we are using our intellect; this happens in the third step, called *abstraction*. So knowledge involves a three-step process leading to understanding: sensation through external senses, imagination through internal phantasms, and abstraction through the intellect. Let us discuss these three steps briefly, without going into all the details of Aquinas's epistemology—they are quite complex, and also not fully relevant to our purpose.

The first step, sensation, is crucial for Aquinas's epistemology. He insists that the soul, which includes the intellect, would have no use for the body if, as Plato held, all knowledge were derived from the mind alone. In other words, he contradicts Plato in asserting that there is nothing in the mind that was not first in the senses. The senses are at the basis of all empirical knowledge. Aquinas likes to say, "Whatever is can be known." He basically asserts that sensation is a passive reception through the senses and cannot err, but perception is an active process of the intellect. In other words, he would attribute something like optical illusions to faulty perception, not faulty sensation. That makes sense, for illusions do not disappear or diminish simply because we know they are illusions.

The second step, imagination, is also essential, for it is impossible for the intellect to understand anything without forming phantasms, that is, mental images. By "phantasm," Aquinas means any recalled image, sound, smell, taste, or touch—i.e., any recalled sensory experience. Call them fantasies of the imagination, if you wish. The phantasm is a product of sense data gathered through the senses, and it acts as the raw material upon which the intellect operates. It is like a photograph that is comprehensible to us because it more or less resembles the image of a scene as it appears on the retina. Phantasms are images with which we "imagine" that which we try to understand. In his *Summa Theologiae*, Aquinas quotes Aristotle: "The soul understands nothing without a phantasm." Do not take them as mere pictures or replicas, for then "wolf," "organism," and "animal" could not differ from each other, as they would all be abstracted from the very same phantasm. So it is probably safer to call a phantasm a mental impression, rather than a mental image. The phantasm puts form and structure into the sensation, and thus identifies the likenesses of individuals.

The phantasm always represents a particular, concrete individual—that is, one particular wolf, organism, animal, or whatever. So the phantasms that we form are not universal knowledge yet. If we were to equate our mental images with universal knowledge, then we would be confronted with the problem of how to deal with the ideas formed by people who were actually misled, confused, or even irrational. If all phantasms were to count as knowledge, we would fall into a radical subjectivism in which there is no objective standard of truth.

The third step, abstraction, raises the phantasm to the level of real knowledge. It results in the formation of ideas of universals, that is, of ideas that define objects according to their essential qualities. It sees the likenesses of essences. For the sake of simplicity, call them definitions if you wish—definitions that categorize sense data by disregarding certain differences. Our knowledge of things, obviously, is not the same as knowledge of our phantasms. Rather, the phantasms are the means by which we come to understand things. Phantasms are still concrete, individual, singular, and particular—whereas knowledge is abstract and universal. Knowledge of individuals is prior to knowledge of universals. But any knowledge that is to count as real knowledge, in Aquinas's view, must be universal. Thus we can consider the nature of a horse, for instance, while disregarding the fact that this horse is here before us now and has a certain color, weight, and so forth. In knowing and defining natural substances, be they human beings or horses, we must include flesh and bones—but not this particular flesh and these particular bones. In a word, the abstract is derived from the concrete, the universal is derived from the singular, the unchanging is derived from the changing.

What might be surprising is that Aquinas is in fact saying that all knowledge worth the name "knowledge" is necessarily abstract. Yet, it remains true that there is not an idea in the mind, however vaporously abstract it might be, whose origins are not ultimately rooted in sensation. All knowledge is based on the senses—it is about reality, not about knowledge. To know is to know things, not to know mental abstractions. Aquinas's epistemological theory would later be classified as empiricism, as it claims that sensations are a necessary step in acquiring knowledge. No perception without sensation, so to speak. The fact that eyes and ears exist points to the existence of shapes and colors, or of sounds and noise—unless we want to consider eyes and ears as useless whimsies of nature.

But there is more to human knowledge. Since we are rational animals, we have not only an intellect to understand the things around us, but also reason (*ratio*) that gives us the capacity of reasoning. Aquinas clearly distinguishes reason from intellect, without setting them apart. He distinguished two ways of knowing: one way is knowing through the senses (followed by processing by the intellect), and the other way is knowing by reasoning. The intellect, on the one hand, knows without reasoning; it knows the truth intuitively and directly (*sine discursu*). The *ratio*, on the other hand, knows through reasoning; it knows the truth indirectly (*per discursum*). Rationality—the capacity of reasoning—involves the back and forth of argument moving from one thing known to another, and then advancing in knowledge by such movement. It leads us from one idea to a related idea. It even allows for hypothetical reasoning, which is widely used in science. Weighing evidence and coming to a conclusion are rational activities par excellence. Reasoning is the natural activity by way of which we organize our experiences, whereas the intellect enables us to discern the truth within them.

For Aquinas, reason is natural for our species, because it is what a human being needs to make free choices. Aquinas thus accepts Aristotle's notion that rationality is the essence of a human being, although Aquinas does not equate man's entire essence with rationality. Yet, Aquinas calls us rational animals because rationality sets us apart from other animals. Animals may certainly be more or less intelligent, but they are not rational beings. Animals do have the capacity, though, to sense and remember things, but they lack understanding in the sense of formulating concepts, asking questions, framing propositions, and drawing conclusions.

They show no signs of abstract reasoning or having reasons for their "thoughts" (if they have any); they do not think in terms of true and false; they do not think in terms of cause and effect with "if-then" statements or "if-and-only-if" statements. Instead, they are "moved" by motives, drives, instincts, emotions, stimuli, and training, but not by reason and/or intellect. In other words, animals do not have a mind endowed with the capacity for rationality and intellect—regardless of their intelligence.

There is a striking similarity here between this and another distinction—the one between signals and symbols. Symbols refer, whereas signals do not. It does not matter whether we train a dog with a command like "here!" or a command like "Hector!" The dog reacts to these signals the same way, not realizing that the latter command refers to himself. For animals, both commands work through association, but only humans know how different they are. Animals cannot make this distinction, so they treat everything in their surroundings as signals that call for a direct and definite response. Animals are "born positivists"—they take everything at face value. Humans, on the other hand, deal with things after making a "detour," through symbols and concepts; they assign various interpretations to the things they see. They move from the world of sensible singulars (things, events, and signals) to the world of immaterial universals (concepts and symbols). Whereas signals have their own intrinsic properties, symbols have a wider meaning and interpretation.

Animals do not have the capacity to understand symbols. When we warn a dog by pointing a finger at an approaching car, the dog just looks at the finger—and may even lick it—but it does not get what the finger refers to; it cannot make various interpretations. For animals, a pointing finger is not a symbol, but just what it is, a finger (although they can be trained to associate this with something else as a signal). The pointing finger just cannot direct the animal's attention to something beyond itself, for that requires interpretation. A prey animal, for example, can take a predator only as a signal to flee or attack, not as a symbol with various interpretations. It cannot see a predator as an animal in need, an animal born to prey on others, an animal brought up that way, an addicted killer, a preprogrammed killer, a member of a larger conspiracy, an inevitable part of life, or a part of nature that needs to be preserved. Humans can come up with such different interpretations, but animals cannot, for they see only signals that call for an immediate response (sure, we do too sometimes). Symbols, on the other hand, are part of reasoning and refer to things around us in a specific context.

Whereas reasoning is pondering realities beyond that which is experienced through the senses, animals, on the contrary, seem to live their lives entirely in the present, without having any thoughts about the past or the future—perhaps memories, but not thoughts, symbols, or interpretations. If pets have a pedigree, it is thanks to their owners; if they have birthdays, wish lists, appointments, or schedules, it is because their owners create those; and if they have graves, those were dug by their owners as well. Cats or dogs have never come up with the thought of going to the pet store and buying their own food, let alone of starting their own pet store.

We said earlier that it is intellect—not intelligence—that makes our world intelligible. Whereas intelligence can be graded on an IQ scale, intellect cannot. One can have more or less intelligence, but one cannot have more or less intellect (in the sense we are using here). Intelligence only works with perception of sense data. Consequently, animals may show various forms of intelligence in their behavior, because intelligence is a brain feature and as such an important tool in survival. We find spatial intelligence in pigeons and bats, social intelligence in wolves and monkeys, formal intelligence in apes and dolphins, practical intelligence in rats and ravens, to name just a few. Intelligence is a matter of processing sense data—something even a robot can do by "cleverly" processing sounds, images, stimuli, signals, and the like.

Intellect, on the other hand, is very different from this. Like intelligence, intellect also uses sense data, but unlike intelligence, it changes perception into cognition by means of intellectual concepts and logical reasoning, which make sensorial experiences intelligible for us. Thanks to cognition, we can even detect illusions in our perceptions (yet illusions do not disappear or diminish simply because we know they are illusions). Because concepts are irreducible to images or phantasms, any strictly intellectual activity, although grounded in sensation and imagination, ultimately surpasses sensation and imagination.

Before we end this discussion, let me stress that Aquinas's discussion of our human capacity for knowledge occurs within the context of his discussion of the human soul (*anima*). This fact is significant, for it indicates that Aquinas believes that *ratio* and intellect are not capacities separate from the soul but components of the soul itself. They are not even different capacities, strictly speaking. So the human mind with its *ratio* and intellect is the intellectual part of the human soul—and this soul is the *form* of the body. Hence, *ratio* and intellect are not part of the body itself. The trouble of claiming otherwise—of claiming that they are located in our genes or in any other part of the body—is that such a claim would cut off our reason for reasoning and for trusting our own *ratio* and intellect. That would amount to mental suicide.

A Foundation for Science

How does all of this apply to the sciences as we know them today? Science makes use of our senses in its collection of data, and it uses intellectual concepts and rational logic to come to conclusions. Once we begin questioning the trustworthiness of our brains and senses and reason, there is no way of establishing their trustworthiness again independently of trusting them. Any sort of skepticism regarding our senses, our intellect, and our reasoning eats away at the foundation of science. If one generates a scientific conclusion that is, in turn, used to nullify the trustworthiness of our senses, we destroy the very scientific conclusion we had come up with, because all scientific conclusions depend on experimental data that in turn depend on our senses. That is why Aquinas stresses that knowledge arises entirely from the senses and moves from the particular to the general, not the other way around. Sense data have priority. Needless to say, the power of the senses has been enormously advanced by telescopes and microscopes and other sophisticated observational tools. However, that makes his case even stronger.

The enterprise of science relies on the trusting of "eyewitness" reports of observed data, largely in the case of special experiences and experiments. Most of what we know about science and its findings is from hearsay, based on expert reports. The scientists involved must conduct some experiment to gather data, whether the experiment is simple (such as dropping a ball and timing its fall) or complex (such as searching for the infamous and enigmatic Higgs boson). They are essential eyewitnesses. But the term "eyewitness" might be misleading. What scientists report as the result of an experiment is not a recital of observations they have made. It is rather an *interpretation* of these observations, by transposing them into the abstract, symbolic world of theories by means of abstraction. But Aquinas would emphatically add that, no matter how abstract, all observation still remains ultimately rooted in reality, in sensorial experiences. G. K. Chesterton rightly noticed that Aquinas "is arguing for the popular proverbs that seeing is believing; that the proof of the pudding is in the eating."

Based on the senses and on human intellect and reasoning, any scientist is able to gradually understand the universe better and better. These human "tools" give them access to the laws of nature and the structure of this universe. But this raises the question of what we are to make of all those scientific explanations that are based on scientific laws. They explain material things and events, and yet they use nonmaterial laws of nature to do so. Right in the middle of our comfortable, spacious, temporal, transient, and piecemeal world of material things, something pops up that we call "laws of nature"—physical laws, Mendelian laws, economic laws, and so forth. Unlike all material things surrounding us, laws do not have any of the features that apply to the material world—that's right, none. "Laws" are just abstractions from a concrete physical reality that behaves in accordance with the laws from which this concrete physical reality itself comes. Laws tell us how things in this universe act and operate.

A law such as the law of gravity, for instance, is not located somewhere in space, not even in our minds, for that is just a mental version of the law—a law itself is "everywhere." In a physical sense, laws are nowhere, and yet they are everywhere and apply to the entire universe; they are general and universal. Laws are also beyond time—timeless entities that cannot emerge or perish in the history of the universe; we may discover them at a certain time, but they were already there before we discovered them. And laws are not subject to change, for they will always remain true, and were always true, even before we came to know them. And here is the most important difference: Not only are laws general, as we find the same law applied all over the universe, over and over again, but they also are necessary, which means that things in this universe cannot be different from what is expressed in those laws of nature. That makes them general, even universal.

Scientific laws, or laws of nature, are pivotal for science. Very few will deny the validity of physical laws. Yet, they reveal something enigmatic about this universe: it is not a chaotic entity. Einstein was right when he wrote, "But surely, a priori, one should expect the world to be chaotic, not to be grasped by thought in any way." And yet, we seem to be able to grasp and comprehend the world to a certain extent. It has an *order* that seems to be built-in—not an order imposed by scientists but an order that is unveiled by them. And scientists are even able to unveil this order such that we can understand it. Albert Einstein also used to say that the most incomprehensible thing about the universe is that it is comprehensible; he actually spoke of a mystery. It is indeed incomprehensible that we can, at least in principle, comprehend the universe. Somehow the order we discover in science is rational and logical. Even the physicist Paul Davies said at one point, "There must be an unchanging rational ground in which the logical, orderly nature of the universe is rooted."

When John Stuart Mill says, "It is a law that every event depends on some law," we should wonder whether he ever wondered where that law itself then came from (other than from himself). Indeed, it is a fundamental "rule" in science that everything it tries to explain or predict can be described in the form of laws—laws of physics, chemistry, biology, and so on. Everything in this universe seems to act in a "lawful" way, and not in a whimsical way. But the fundamental question is where such a "rule" of "law and order" in the universe comes from. The "law" that everything is based on laws definitely does not come from science itself. Science can explain things by using laws, but it certainly cannot explain the very existence of those laws. So where do they come from then? The only rational answer seems to be this: the "law and order" of our universe is not an a priori assumption—rooted in the way we think about the world, à la Kant—but rather it is a *given*, rooted in the way the world is owing to the way it was created.

As we discussed earlier, a general statement such as "all iron expands with temperature" requires more and more cases for its confirmation; a statement like this is based on generalizations. But there are also universal principles such as "expanding iron has a cause" that are not of an empirical, inductive nature and are true independently of inductive confirmation. How can they be so comprehensive and general, even universal, and yet so true and certain? The answer is that they are not based on empirical generalizations. Michael Augros uses a good analogy from mathematics: "I have not inspected every instance of the number six, yet I am convinced . . . that the general statement 'Every six is even' admits no exception. I am not worried that someone in Australia has an odd six in his pocket."

On their own, though, universal principles do not get us far, for they are independent of any specific experience and are "immune" to the influx of new experiences. In order to give them "body and flesh," we need to delve further into experience—and that's where science comes in. But science can begin only after these universal principles have been asserted. Universal principles are not the outcome of scientific research but a precondition for scientific research—they come from metaphysics, not science.

To put this in more technical terms, the idea of laws in nature is a given—we read them from the nature of things. Science cannot explain the existence of laws but needs them for its explanations. Somehow they were "engraved" in the universe, making the universe look more like "a great thought than a great machine," in the words of the late astrophysicist Sir James Jeans. It is this "great thought" that scientists try to decipher. Isaac Newton said something similar when he stated that the solar system "could only proceed from the dominion of an intelligent and powerful Being."

The mystery we have here is the fact that the rationality present in our minds matches the rationality we find in the world. It would be easy to explain this correspondence by stating that we project our rationality into the world, but that contradicts the fact that we constantly need to adjust the "speculations" in our minds to the "data" of reality. Aquinas would counter that we cannot just mold our sensorial experiences to our reason-seeking will, because the phenomena we encounter resist our attempts to bend them to our prior expectations. So there must be another explanation for this mysterious conformity between the rationality of our minds and the rationality found around us.

The best, and arguably only, explanation for this conformity must lie in some more profound reason. As John Polkinghorne puts it, "Such a reason would be provided by the Rationality of the Creator." Without God's thought, there would be only mere chaos, or actually nothing. In other words, science is a work of the mind—not just ours but first of all God's. We could even go so far as to claim that without a Creator God, scientists would lose their reason for trusting their own scientific reasoning. The mere fact that reason exists—including its order, its contents, its principles, its rules, and its power—calls for an explanation. Reason tells us that only reasoned proofs and scientific evidence make our claims understandable, intelligible, justified, and true. Science itself arises from and rests upon this foundation—the certainty and strength of reason and its many principles and demands. If these were based only on individual, subjective, and personal sensations, we would lose the universal rational order that guides and evaluates all our thinking and all our scientific endeavors. We would end up with mere illusions or hallucinations.

Thus, the pivotal question is what causes reason's order to exist. Leaving God out of the cosmos would reduce reason to a mere neural experience that leaves us only with the sensation of reason, without any underlying reality. If God does exist, on the other hand, there is at least an explanation and foundation for the existence of reason and its order—which is so vital to science. It would arguably be the best explanation for this mysterious conformity between the rationality of our minds and the rationality found in the world around us.

The matter of *truth* is another crucial issue in science. Science is in fact one of the strongholds where truth is still respected in our culture. The much heralded idea of falsification says that a theory is in trouble when its predictions turn out to be false—that is, not true. This raises the question: What is this truth—how can it be defined and how can it be determined? Aquinas holds a very safe and sound view of truth, the same view Aristotle had promoted—sometimes called the *correspondence* theory: "To say of what is that it is and of what is not that it is not, is true." Aquinas, in turn, speaks of a correspondence between reality and intellect (*adequatio intellectus et rei*). This may sound trivial, but it basically asserts that any true understanding of reality has to correspond to that reality. Compared to rival theories—the consensus theory and the coherence theory—it is arguably the best definition of truth. Let us see why its rivals fail.

The *consensus* theory considers statements true, not because they correspond to what is going on in reality, but because most of us accept them as true. A common reason for accepting them as true is that they "work" in a satisfactory manner, which is the standpoint of pragmatism. This theory confirms that true explanations are indeed successful, but its problem is that successful explanations are not necessarily true. Ptolemy's geocentrism was highly successful, but not true. Besides, even success depends ultimately on truth in Aquinas's sense, since success implies that a prediction corresponds to what is actually taking place in reality. So that takes us back to the correspondence theory.

Another theory, the *coherence* theory, declares a statement true when it is part of a coherent axiomatic system. However, this would entail that a statement being true in one system may be untrue in another system. Consequently, this kind of truth is self-made, depending on the chosen axioms. This idea may be helpful in mathematics and logic, but it is rather useless in empirical sciences. Whether we choose a Euclidean or a Riemannian geometry may be completely up to us, but when it comes to cosmology, we need the kind of geometry that corresponds with reality and matches the facts best. The problem is that the choice between coherent systems cannot be made on the basis of coherence but must be made on the basis of correspondence again.

This conclusion—that truth is ultimately based on correspondence—is probably something that practically all modern scientists would agree with, although perhaps not wholeheartedly. They do in fact maintain, as a working assumption, that they are dealing with objective reality, even though they do not always say so. Although some sociobiologists seem to claim that we believe what we believe because what we call "truth" emerges from brains shaped by natural selection, they must admit that natural selection itself operates according to the way the world "is." Besides, if their claim entails that our beliefs are mere artifacts, such a claim would act like a boomerang that destroys its own truth claims. Beliefs like these contradict the fact that scientific proofs of something being true come from conformity with reality, not from systems of ideas. Regardless of the fact that neither human reason nor the universe can be explained by themselves, the most surprising thing in all of this remains the perfect harmony of thought and being, truth and reality. Perhaps the only possible explanation would be that we have here "a match made in heaven."

As to the issue of truth, it is safe to say that Aquinas uses a solid theory to define truth (how to determine truth is another issue). It is clear again that Aquinas strives for real and objective knowledge—a perfect harmony of thought and being, truth and reality, that is. His epistemology is firmly based on senses, intellect, and reason—on things we all have in common. We have no direct access to what the world is "really" like other than through our senses. Yet our knowledge is real, truthful, reliable, and "veridical"—after being tested versus reality, of course. This viewpoint should not be confused with "naive realism," which assumes that perceptions based on the senses are direct recordings of reality. If that were the case, all we would need to do to perceive is to take a "picture" of it. However, the mind with its intellect does not simply record an exact picture of the world but creates its own "picture." Perception is not a passive monitoring process of sense data but rather the result of some mental reconstruction process. Therefore, it is the realism of Aristotle's and Aquinas's epistemology that we need as an antidote against philosophers like Hume and Kant. Even though our perceptions are mental and intellectual constructions rather than direct recordings of reality, they clearly are neither arbitrary nor illusory.

The need for a sound epistemology was very well expressed by Albert Einstein when he said, "Epistemology without contact with science becomes an empty scheme. Science without epistemology is—insofar as it is thinkable at all—primitive and muddled." As usual, Chesterton put this in a nutshell when he said, "The Pragmatist sets out to be practical, but his practicality turns out to be entirely theoretical. The Thomist begins by being theoretical, but his theory turns out to be entirely practical. That is why a great part of the world is returning to it today."

To open the mind for further study:

Bochenski, Joseph M. *The Road to Understanding: More Than Dreamt of in Your Philosophy.* North Andover, MA: Genesis Publishing Company, 1996.

Koterski, Joseph W. *An Introduction to Medieval Philosophy.* Malden, MA: Wiley-Blackwell, 2009.

Owens, Joseph. *Cognition: An Epistemological Enquiry.* Houston, TX: Center for Thomistic Studies, 1992.

Verschuuren, Gerard M. *The Destiny of the Universe: In Pursuit of the Great Unknown.* St. Paul, MN: Paragon House, 2014.

5

Aquinas and the Sciences

EVEN THOSE who praise Aquinas for his contributions to philosophy and theology remain skeptical about his contributions to, or even involvement with, the (natural) sciences. They point out, for instance, that Aquinas was much less actively involved with the sciences than one of his main teachers, Albert the Great (*Albertus Magnus*). Indeed, unlike his student, Albert had quite a track record for his time: he discovered the element arsenic; he experimented with photosensitive chemicals, including silver nitrate; and he made disciplined observations of plant anatomy and animal embryology.

This is one of the main reasons why it has become the fashion in modern academia to discount Aquinas's understanding of science as outdated and incorrect. He is sometimes even denigrated as a "geocentrist." Other reasons for scoffing at Aquinas certainly are the lack of familiarity with his philosophy among modern scientists and the difficulty of grasping and understanding his work, even in translation.

Aquinas the Scientist?

Nevertheless, there are several reasons why this skepticism about Aquinas's contributions to the (natural) sciences is not fully justified. First of all, what we consider science nowadays was just in its beginning stages. The term "scientist" did not even exist until 1833. Originally, the term "science" (*scientia*) simply meant "knowledge." For Aquinas, science included metaphysics—in line with Aristotle, who called it the "queen of sciences." But it also included other sciences. Like Aristotle, Aquinas held that there is a plurality of both theoretical and practical sciences. Ethics, economics, and politics were the practical sciences, while physics, mathematics, and metaphysics were considered the theoretical sciences.

However, soon the scientific method would change things by creating an empirical enterprise that, unlike the rest of philosophy, was based on experiments. By the end of the eighteenth century, this experimental enterprise had begun to be called "science" to distinguish it from philosophy, and then William Whewell coined the term "scientist" for the person who practiced it. From then on, metaphysics referred to philosophical enquiry of a "nonempirical" character into the nature of existence and being. Although the term "science" is often thought of as applying narrowly to the natural sciences, it pertains, in its broader sense, to any systematically arranged branch of knowledge. If we consider this broader sense, Aquinas was very much involved with science, although the nature of his involvement was more theoretical than practical. Stanley Jaki acknowledged that Aquinas did not "put his foot inside the gates of a science better than that of Aristotle. But he certainly pioneered a crucial phase of the march toward those gates." When Aquinas taught that it is intrinsically impossible for planets and stars to move in straight lines, he was not, in Jaki's words, endorsing that point "as of intrinsic necessity but as factuality suggested by the science of his time."

This should not give us the impression, though, that there were no natural sciences during the Late Middle Ages. It is actually amazing how someone like the astronomer Carl Sagan, in one of his books, makes it look as if nothing happened in the natural sciences between AD 415 and AD 1543. That is just historical ignorance. It is becoming more and more evident, and it has been accepted by a growing contingent of historians, that science was born in the cradle of Judeo-Christian faith, especially during the Late Middle Ages. Here are some of its pioneer crafters: As early as the seventh century, the English Benedictine monk Bede studied the sea's tidal currents. At the end of the first millennium, Pope Sylvester II had already used advanced instruments of astronomical observation, driven by a passion for understanding the order of the universe. He also endorsed and promoted study of arithmetic, mathematics, and astronomy, reintroducing to Europe the abacus and armillary sphere, which had been lost to Europe since the end of the Greco-Roman era. He is also said to be the first to introduce into Europe the decimal numeral system with arabic numerals.

Very often forgotten in this context is Hildegard of Bingen, a Benedictine abbess and Doctor of the Church. In the twelfth century, she wrote botanical and medicinal texts based on the theological notion, ultimately derived from Genesis, that all things put on earth are for the use of humans. She was particularly interested in the healing properties of plants, animals, and stones. During the same time period, Bishop Robert Grosseteste introduced the scientific method, including the concept of falsification, while the Franciscan friar Roger Bacon established concepts such as hypothesis, experimentation, and verification. In other words, the scientific project, even the scientific method itself, was an invention of these Catholic pioneers.

One of the first to realize this was the French physicist Pierre Duhem. When he studied the works of medieval mathematicians and philosophers such as John Buridan, Nicole Oresme, and Roger Bacon, their sophistication surprised him. He consequently came to regard them as the founders of modern science, having in his view anticipated many of the discoveries of Galileo Galilei and later thinkers. Thus, he came to regard the medieval Scholastic tradition of the Catholic Church as the origin of modern science. Many historians of science would later follow his lead.

The second reason why skepticism regarding Aquinas's contributions to the (natural) sciences is not fully warranted is the fact that Aquinas did contribute to some scientific achievements. Though not a scientist in the modern sense, Aquinas did address many problems we would now assign to astronomy, physics, chemistry, and the life sciences. In the study of motion, for instance, he held that velocity is a mode of continuous quantity and thus is capable of intensification in the same manner as qualities. He further taught that if a vacuum were possible, motion through it would still take time, since motion's temporal character does not arise uniquely from external resistance. Both of these teachings led other thinkers to speculate about internal resistances to motion, thus foreshadowing the modern concept of inertia—the most important concept in Newtonian physics and in Einstein's general relativity physics. This concept, clearly articulated in the Middle Ages, was in fact passed on and matured, until finally it was given its complete formulation by more recent physicists. As Jaki put it, "Progress needed a spark, the idea of inertial motion, which is the first and most fundamental of Newton's three laws."

Aquinas did even more for the natural sciences. He regarded gravitation as the natural motion of a heavy object to its natural place but denied that it was caused by some absolute principle. In this he implicitly rejected the absolute space and attractive forces later proposed by Newton's followers, and opted instead for relational concepts that have more affinity to those of modern relativity theory. Aquinas also took up the problems of magnets as well as tidal variations, and he was intent on reducing them to natural, instead of occult, causes. In astronomy, the man who has been vilified as a "geocentrist" voiced his expectation that Ptolemy's theory would one day be superseded by a simpler explanation, since all such theories are based on hypothetical reasoning. In his own words, "Maybe the phenomena of the stars can be explained by some other schema not yet discovered by men." In the life sciences, he wrote a treatise on the heart in an attempt to trace lines of causality of blood in motion.

One could even make the case that he touched on chemical issues and thus prepared the ground for chemistry. Based on the doctrine of so-called *minima naturalia* (the smallest parts into which a homogeneous natural substance could be divided while still retaining its essential character), he indirectly contributed to the development of atomistic, corpuscular theories in science. He taught how elements are present in compounds, holding that they are not present there actually or potentially, but only virtually (see chapter 3). So, while there is only one substance that results from the composition of various elements, the new substance has the combined powers of the elements that came together in its composition—which makes for a new compound, instead of a mixture of the original elements.

To use a modern example, when the substances hydrogen and oxygen change into a new substance, water, the change cannot be attributed merely to the rearrangement of the elements involved. The two elements are present in themselves as gases before change takes place. Since change does occur, some different substance comes to be. If it were the elements that caused the change, two gases in themselves would be substantially the same as water, which they are not. Besides, hydrogen and oxygen can be rearranged to make things other than water, e.g., hydrogen peroxide. These elements in themselves are not the reason why hydrogen and oxygen when combined produce water. The essence of water is different from the essence of either hydrogen or oxygen, and each of these essences is different from the other. In other words, although Aquinas did not work with chemicals, he did prepare the future analyses of such work.

A third reason for rejecting the claim that Aquinas did not contribute to the advancement of science is the fact that his epistemology gave all human knowledge, which includes science, a firm empirical basis. In addition, he saw very clearly the possibility of a science that does not depend on divine revelation but is based merely on sensorial experience and the intellectual processing of that experience. This opened the way for an autonomous, rational enterprise called science. Besides, he also anticipated its future diversity. The different scientific disciplines we know nowadays are generated by the fact that we can consider the things of nature from different perspectives. Aquinas holds that the division of sciences can be accounted for by the power of *abstraction*, which allows the intellect to leave out of consideration certain characteristics (see chapter 4). Social scientists, for instance, can study behavioral processes of human beings while ignoring and abstracting from physiological processes such as heartbeat. It is also through abstraction that the knowledge of a single individual human being, based on concrete sensorial experience, can become usable for *all* human beings. Even the technique of representative sampling, for instance, is based on this idea. All of this makes science a universal enterprise.

A fourth reason would be the following. Although Aquinas may have had a rather indirect impact on the development of the sciences, it was nevertheless influential. Aquinas was a dynamically original thinker who would today refer to Darwin and Einstein as avidly as he employed the Aristotelian science of his day. Christianity had already provided the cultural conditions for the emergence of modern science in the Western world, and Aquinas would further solidify science's philosophical foundation, so his work in fact prepared the ground for the upcoming advancement of the natural sciences. A key point in his philosophy is the statement that there is an objective order of things (see chapter 4). All natural explanations of the world—whether in cosmology (see chapter 6) or in evolution (see chapter 9)—must assume that ultimately the order of nature is the unexplained ground of all explanation. It is basically the biblical idea that the Creator arranged everything according to weight, measure, and number (cf. Ws 11:20). We are dealing here with a universal principle, in Aquinas's view. The sciences could never operate without principles like this.

The Power of Reason

Aquinas argues that we can have a true knowledge of the world without resorting to faith, because "the human mind can see the truth by natural light without anything being added." Thanks to the power of reason, nature can be studied apart from faith without becoming a threat to faith (see chapter 2). No wonder many scholars trace the origins of modern science back to this quest for studying and interpreting nature according to rational laws of cause and effect. Aquinas recognized that a world in which the natural processes are explicable in their own terms does not challenge the role of the Creator. So philosophy and religion had nothing to fear from the upcoming sciences. It is very doubtful whether science could have ever flourished outside the cradle of Christianity and Christian philosophy—in particular the philosophy of Aquinas. They both provided a framework, even a hotbed, for the future advancement of science.

It could be argued that a tendency toward a different conception of divine causality is part of what distinguishes Judeo-Christian religion from other religions—and it might explain why natural science improved in the West and weakened, or even was lacking, in the rest of the world. It was the Christian and Thomistic understanding that the world is both good and intelligible to us that laid the foundation for science and helped Western society to pass onto successive generations the discoveries that were made. Pagan cultures, on the other hand, had created a view of the world that inhibited scientific advancement, as they did not view the world as rational. They viewed things as being controlled by many, even whimsical, gods and magical powers. They did not view the world as something that was governed by laws of nature accessible to the human mind and waiting for discovery.

More specifically, it is the Judeo-Christian concept of a Creator God that forms the cornerstone of all of the above. Belief in a Creator God entails that nature is not a divine but a created entity; nature is not divine in itself, only its Maker is—which opens the door for scientific exploration (otherwise we would not be allowed to "touch" the divine). Because the Judeo-Christian God is a reliable God—not confined inside the Aristotelian box, not capricious like the Olympians in ancient Greece, and not entirely beyond human comprehension like in Islam—the world depends on the laws that God has laid down in creation. Thanks to God's creation, everything else has lost its power, has lost its divine allure. Faith in the one God changes the universe, once inhabited by spirits and deities, into something "rational." In this view, only God is the source from which the order as well as the intelligibility of the universe ultimately stem.

In other words, it is the Judeo-Christian view that the universe is the creation of a rational Intellect that is capable of being rationally interrogated by all human beings, including the scientists among them. Jews and Christians realize that their rational God has made a universe of uniform laws on which they can rely with their own rational minds, in imitation of the mind of God. Many believers see all of this in the context of God's reliability and trustworthiness, sealed in His covenant with us. In contrast, nature remains an enigma as long as it is ruled by whimsical deities, chaotic powers, or our own philosophical decrees and regulations. Stanley L. Jaki used the phrase "stillbirths of science" in reference to the ancient cultures of Egypt, China, India, Babylon,

Greece, and Arabia. Their cyclical worldviews—a "cosmic tread-mill" in Jaki's words—prevented the breakthrough of science as a self-sustaining discipline. Jaki claimed that science—as a universal discipline in which one discovery leads to another, and laws of physics and systems of laws are established—was born of Christianity. In his own words, "Within the biblical world view it was ultimately possible to assume that the heavens and the earth are ruled by the same laws. But it was not possible to do this within the world vision that dominated all other ancient cultures. In all of them the heavens were divine."

Although Aristotle, for example, did make some significant discoveries, his classical Greek culture was unable to maintain and nurture further development. His animistic view of physics led him to conclude that if two bodies were dropped from the same height on earth, the one with twice the weight of the other would fall twice as fast because it had twice the nature and twice the desire to seek its place. The pagan culture he lived in obviously had taken its toll. If the world is controlled by the whim of combative, immature, and impulsive pagan gods or by the pantheism of an eternal cosmic cycle, then there would be no real laws of nature to discover. Jaki again: "Within the Greek ambiance it was impossible, in fact it would have been a sacrilege, to assume that the motion of the moon and the fall of an apple were governed by the same law. It was, however, possible for Newton, because he was the beneficiary of the age-old Christian faith."

The same holds for other civilizations. When the Jesuits went to China, they were amazed at the Asians' lack of progress in their understanding of the world. These cultures contributed talent and ingenuity, but scientific enterprise came to a standstill. In other words, the modern physical sciences were, in fact, made possible by the religious setting from which they emerged. To hold that the world is created is to accept, simultaneously, the two assumptions required for science, namely, that the universe is not divine and that it is marked, through and through, by order and intelligibility. If the world or nature is considered divine, then one would never allow oneself to analyze it, dissect it, or perform experiments upon it, and all incentives for doing science would be suppressed. But a created world, by definition, is not divine. It is other than God, and in that very otherness, scientists find their freedom to act (see chapter 3). At the same time, if the world were unintelligible, no science would get off the ground, since all science is based upon the assumption that nature can be known and understood by the human mind. No matter how empirical and experimental the modern sciences are, the human mind with its intellect and reasoning remains in charge by inventing experiments based on theoretical reasoning and by informing the senses regarding what to pay attention to.

If this is true, we must come to an astounding conclusion: all scientists live off Judeo-Christian capital, whether they like it or not. Even the late nuclear physicist J. Robert Oppenheimer, who was not a Christian, was ready to acknowledge this very fact when he said, "Christianity was needed to give birth to modern science." Science was born at the end of what so many consider the "dark" Middle Ages. But in fact, this period marked the beginning of the modern era—it was then that the first universities arose and Aquinas came along. The Middle Ages were of course Catholic, so these first universities of the world were Catholic universities. They were the hotbed for a period of great technological and scientific advancements, as well as achievements in nearly all other fields. Amazingly and unfortunately, many scientists ignore, or even deny, this fact. When you think that what you have is all there is, you do not know what you are missing. Those who live in ignorance do not know that they do; if they were capable of knowing that, they would no longer be ignorant. When Alfred North Whitehead told his Harvard audience in 1925 that modern science was a product of Christianity, his remarks were greeted with surprise. Yet, we cannot cut off the roots from which we came.

Before we further discuss the various sciences as we know them today, I need to clear the path a bit more. Scientists constantly run into discussions and disagreements with fellow scientists—that's what makes science advance. Science is by nature a work in progress. But sometimes scientists also get into philosophical and metaphysical debates—often without even knowing it, because they often lack the knowledge, training, and expertise that would allow them to realize that they are entering philosophical territory, where their scientific expertise is no longer adequate. One cannot come up with scientific answers to philosophical questions, or philosophical answers to scientific questions.

In the rest of this book, we will connect the philosophy of Aquinas with the science of today. But we need to be aware that this endeavor operates on two different levels. Metaphysics is never in competition with science, but it approaches phenomena at a different level of analysis. It has a power that no science has. Its claims do not stand or fall with the findings of science, any more than the claims of arithmetic stand or fall with the findings of physics. That would be making a metaphysics out of physics.

An added problem is that not only do questions and answers differ, but also the terms they are phrased in. A superficial reading often leads critics to assume they are addressing the same issues, when in fact they are very often not using the key terms in the same sense. Both physicists and metaphysicians use terms like "cause," "matter," and the like—yet they have a very different meaning. A "vacuum" in physics, for instance, is not the same as "nothing" in metaphysics. And "spontaneity" as used in quantum physics is not the same thing as "uncaused" in metaphysics. Darwin's "cause" is not Aquinas's "cause," and so on.

Very often scientists understand these terms only in their scientific sense and are not aware of their different meaning in metaphysics. Some scientists, especially Nobel laureates, think that their authority in a tiny segment of science entitles them to proclaim authoritative statements about everything else outside that small segment. They often raise question-begging philosophical objections disguised as scientific objections. As long as we are aware of this source of confusion, Aquinas's philosophy will be able to help us analyze and assess current scientific discoveries and claims.

To sum up this chapter, the creation of the university, the commitment to reason and rational argument, and the overall spirit of inquiry that characterized medieval intellectual life and culminated in Aquinas's philosophy amount to what the historian Edward Grant calls "a gift from the Latin Middle Ages to the modern world." The modern world glories in its science, which has allowed us to see to the very edge of the universe, to the beginnings of time, and even to the invisible world that may be the very boundary marker between physics and metaphysics. The gift that Aquinas has given us may never be widely acknowledged; in the words of Edward Grant, the gift from the Latin Middle Ages to the modern world "is a gift that may never be acknowledged. Perhaps it will always retain the status it has had for the past four centuries as the best-kept secret of Western civilization."

To open the mind for further study:

Hannam, James. *The Genesis of Science: How the Christian Middle Ages Launched the Scientific Revolution.* Washington, DC: Regnery Publishing, 2011.

Jaki, Stanley L. *The Savior of Science.* Grand Rapids, MI: Eerdmans, 2000.

Kretzmann, Norman, and Stump, Eleonore. *The Cambridge Companion to Aquinas.* Cambridge University Press, 1993.

Woods, Thomas E., Jr. *How the Catholic Church Built Western Civilization.* Regnery Publishing, 2012.

6

Aquinas and Cosmology

COSMOLOGY means the logos, or rational science, of the cosmos or universe. It used to be a major division of philosophy, but many of its questions—questions about time, space, and matter—have become the focus of modern science and have been answered in what is now called physical cosmology, the branch of physics and astrophysics that deals with the study of the physical origins and evolution of the universe. One of its main issues is the question of whether the universe has a beginning or not—a question that remained undecided for a long time, and that for some still is.

A Beginning of the Universe?

Aquinas did address this issue but was not really concerned about the answer to this question. Aquinas saw no logical contradiction in the notion of an eternal created universe. In his philosophy, an eternal universe would be no less dependent upon God than a universe that has a beginning of time. Even if there has always been a universe and it never "began," it can only exist at any moment in time because God is causing it to, says Aquinas (see chapter 3). He was right; it could be physically possible, for instance, that explosions and collapses follow each other in an endless sequence. If so, the universe might never have had a beginning, but this would not have prevented it from being created.

But although Aquinas thought that, in principle, reason alone cannot conclude definitively as to whether or not the universe had a beginning, he did believe that it was a matter of biblical revelation that the world is *not* eternal. Aquinas realized that there are two related senses of creation, one philosophical, the other theological. The Bible and theology seemed to indicate that the universe did have a beginning. In 1215, the Fourth Lateran Council had solemnly proclaimed that God created all that is "from nothing" (*de nihil condidit*) and that this creation occurred "at the beginning of time" (*ab initio temporis*). As William E. Carroll remarks, "It was the genius of Aquinas to distinguish between creation understood philosophically, with no reference to temporality, and creation understood theologically, which included, among other things, the recognition that the universe does have an absolute temporal beginning." Strangely enough, nowadays it seems that science is confirming that the universe does have a temporal beginning.

Modern science tells us that our universe most likely started with the Big Bang, some fourteen billion years ago. In 1929, Edwin Hubble discovered that the distances to faraway galaxies were generally proportional to their red shifts—an idea originally suggested in 1927 by the Belgian priest, astronomer, and physicist Georges Lemaître of the Catholic University of Louvain. Hubble's observation was taken to indicate that all very distant galaxies and clusters have an apparent velocity directly away from our vantage point; the farther away, the higher their apparent velocity. In 1931, Lemaître went even further and suggested that the evident expansion of the universe, if projected back in time, meant that the further in the past, the smaller the universe was, until at some finite time in the past, all the mass of the universe was concentrated into a single point, a "primeval atom," where and when the fabric of time and space must have started.

Interestingly enough, in the footsteps of Aristotle, Aquinas postulated that there is an ultimate stuff that underlies the radical potency of everything (eventually and theoretically) to turn into anything else. This ultimate stuff he and Aristotle called "prime matter." Prime matter, on its own, is without any distinction; it is not a substance, and does not exist apart from any particular substance; it is mere potentiality as such. It exists only in actual determinate things as the radical potency to undergo limitless changes. Prime matter is only and always found with some substantial form that gives it determination. Yet, although it never exists in and of itself, prime matter is real: it is a real principle of change; it is the real potency that every material thing has in order to undergo an indefinite amount of change. Given his studies as a priest, Lemaître was very familiar with Aquinas. His notion of a "primeval atom" may be a reminder of this. Let us leave it at that.

The English astronomer and mathematician Fred Hoyle is credited with coining the term "Big Bang" during a 1949 radio broadcast. Currently, the Big Bang theory is the prevailing cosmological model that explains the early development of the universe. According to this theory, the universe was once in an extremely hot and dense state, and then expanded rapidly. This rapid expansion caused the universe to cool and resulted in its present state of continuous expansion. Once it had cooled sufficiently, its energy was able to be converted into various subatomic particles, including protons, neutrons, and electrons. Giant clouds of these primordial elements would then coalesce through gravity to form stars and galaxies, and the heavier elements would be synthesized either within stars or during supernovae. Interestingly enough, the ninety-two elements we find on earth can be found all over the universe, indicating a common origin.

A combination of observation and theory suggests that the first quasars and galaxies were formed about a billion years after the Big Bang, and since then larger structures have been forming, such as galaxy clusters and superclusters. Populations of stars have been aging and evolving, so that distant galaxies (which are observed as they were in the early universe) appear very different from nearby galaxies (observed in a more recent state). Moreover, galaxies formed rather recently appear markedly different from galaxies formed at similar distances but shortly after the Big Bang.

Cosmologists now routinely entertain elaborate scenarios to describe what the universe was like when it was the size of a softball. The description of the emergence of four fundamental forces and twelve discrete subatomic particles is almost commonplace in modern physics. There is little doubt among scientists that we live in the aftermath of a giant explosion that occurred around fourteen billion years ago. Although nothing in science is final, the Big Bang theory is still the latest and best we have.

The introduction of the Big Bang theory has made quite an impact not only on cosmology but also on philosophy and theology. If we have to believe some of the leading physicists and astrophysicists nowadays, then the Big Bang story is the modern, "up-to-date" replacement for the "old" creation story, leaving no room for a Creator behind this universe. There are several ways they have come up with the idea that "creation out of nothing" (*creatio ex nihilo*) is no longer a religious or philosophical concept that requires a Creator. The British cosmologist Stephen Hawking, for instance, talks about the Big Bang in terms of what he calls a "spontaneous" creation: "Because there is a law such as gravity, the universe can and will create itself from nothing. Spontaneous creation is the reason there is something rather than nothing." This in turn made the late astrophysicist Carl Sagan exclaim, in the preface of one of Hawking's books, that such a cosmological model has "left nothing for a creator to do." Others, such as the cosmologist Lee Smolin, also made sure that there is no space left for a Creator by proclaiming that "by definition the universe is all there is, and there can be nothing outside it." Amazing what definitions can do!

What would Aquinas, the master of philosophical distinctions, have to add to this debate? For a more detailed discussion on this subject, I refer the reader again to William E. Carroll (see the reference at the end of this chapter), from whom I have borrowed some great insights. Aquinas would say that when philosophers speak of creation "out of nothing" (*ex nihilo*), they certainly are not talking science. Aquinas makes the important distinction between producing (*facere*) and creating (*creare*). Most people use these two terms interchangeably, but Aquinas advises us to separate them. Science is about "producing" something from some-thing else—it is about changes in this universe. Creation, on the other hand, is about "creating" something from nothing—which is not a change at all; certainly not a change from "nothing" to "something." Aquinas puts it this way: "To create is, properly speaking, to cause or produce the being of things." In other words, God doesn't just take preexisting stuff and fashion it, as does the Demiurge in Plato's *Timaeus*. Nor does He use some something called "nothing" and create the universe out of that. Rather, God calls the universe into existence without using pre-existing space or matter.

Creation is not a change, it's a cause, but of a unique kind—a primary cause (see chapter 3). Therefore, creating something "out of nothing" is not producing something from nothing—which would be a conceptual mistake, for it treats nothing as a something. In contrast, the Christian doctrine of creation *ex nihilo* claims that God made the universe without making it out of anything. Creation has everything to do with the philosophical and theological question of why things exist at all, before they can even undergo change. Therefore, creation—but not the Big Bang—is the reason why there is something rather than nothing (including something such as the law of gravity).

Seen in this light, the idea of a "spontaneous creation" is sheer philosophical magic. For something to create itself, or produce itself, it would have to exist before it came into existence—which is logically and philosophically impossible. How could the uni-verse "create itself" from nothing—let alone cause itself? The law of gravity cannot do the trick, for before the universe could ever create itself, we have to posit laws of physics—which are ulti-mately the set of laws that govern the existing, created universe (see chapter 4). So Hawking is actually saying that laws which have meaning only in the context of an existing universe can gen-erate that universe, including the laws of nature, all by themselves before either exists—which makes for a logical contradiction. Aquinas would join Aristotle in responding that whenever there is a change there must be something that changes, for nothing comes from nothing. Plenty of nothing is still nothing! All change requires an underlying material reality. So it is a mistake—a category mistake, if you will—to use arguments coming from the natural sciences to deny creation.

However, since something cannot come from nothing, the Greek philosophers concluded that the universe is eternal: there can be neither a first nor a last motion. That is the point where Aquinas departed from Aristotle by distinguishing between "cause" in the sense of a natural change of some kind and "cause" in the sense of an ultimate bringing into being of something from no antecedent state whatsoever (see chapter 3). *"Creatio non est mutatio,"* says Aquinas, affirming that the act of creation is not some kind of change. All change requires some underlying material reality. When it comes to a change from one state to another, Aquinas agrees with Aristotle that nothing comes from nothing; there must be some underlying material reality, some potentiality for the new state to come into being. Creation, on the other hand, in the words of William E. Carroll, "is the radical causing of the whole existence of whatever exists. Creation is not a change . . . it does not mean that there is a change from 'nothing' to 'something.'"

This Thomistic concept of "creation from nothing" has apparently eluded many cosmologists. Hawking, as we saw, tells us that gravity would be able to "create" the universe—spontaneously, so to speak. And the British physical chemist Peter Atkins claims that science has a limitless power and must even be able to account for the "emergence of everything from absolutely nothing." In response to such claims, Aquinas would insist upon the distinction between producing and creating, or between changing and creating. Creation does not mean changing a no-thing into a something, or changing something into something else—as chemists change water into hydrogen and oxygen; rather, it means bringing everything into being and existence. In other words, "nothingness" is not a highly unusual kind of exotic "stuff" that is more difficult to observe or measure than other things; it is not some kind of element that has not found a position yet in the periodic table; it is in no way a material thing that can change into something else. Rather, it is actually the absence of anything—and therefore we cannot treat no-thing as a some-thing.

Hawking seems to be vaguely aware that there is indeed a problem here, when he says, "Even if there is only one possible unified theory, it is just a set of rules and equations. What is it that breathes fire into the equations and makes a universe for them to describe? The usual approach of science of constructing a mathematical model cannot answer the questions of why there should be a universe for the model to describe. *Why does the universe go to all the bother of existing?*" (the italics are mine). Translated into Leibniz's metaphysical terminology, this means something like the following: Why is there something rather than nothing? Aquinas would answer that God is the reason why there is something rather than nothing—and that's why we need creation. Those who ignore this question, or deny that there is an answer to it, believe in some kind of "black-box theory"—no further questions asked.

An added problem in this discussion is the fact that the Big Bang theory is not about the very beginning of the Big Bang, or about what happened at "point zero." The model it uses could be represented as a cone having a wide circle at the top—that is, at the point where we currently are—and then narrowing down to the bottom, point zero. In this model, we can use theories about space, time, and gravitation (Einstein's general relativity theory) as well as theories about particles, electromagnetism, and quarks (quantum physics). However, these two sets of theories are at odds with each other. Quantum physics, on the one hand, assumes a framework of space and time for any processes to take place; it deals with small particles when gravitation can practically be neglected. The relativity theory, on the other hand, considers space and time to be a product of matter; it holds for situations where gravitation is considerably strong. Now the following problem arises. When we go down in the "cone"—that is, back in time—distances decrease while density increases. The closer we get to point zero, where all distances are ultimately reduced to zero, density and temperature are so high that quantum theories and gravitation theories need to be combined. Unfortunately, that requires a theory we do not have yet. It is merely the dream of a Grand Unified Theory (GUT) that is not yet available, in spite of many trials made on the "drawing board." Right now, it is doubtful whether the concepts of space and time even apply here.

It is this incompleteness and uncertainty of physics that leaves ample room for speculation. Nevertheless, some cosmologists have come up with all kinds of scenarios about point zero, mostly in an attempt to give a scientific twist to the philosophical concept of creation out of nothing. Alexander Vilenkin has developed an explanation of the Big Bang in terms of "quantum tunneling from nothing"—as a fluctuation of a primal vacuum. Just as subatomic particles appear to emerge spontaneously in vacuums in laboratories, as a result of what some have called "quantum tunneling from nothing," so the whole universe may be the result of a similar process, he believes. But the problem with this view is again that the "vacuum" of modern particle physics, whose "fluctuation" some see as bringing our universe into existence, is not absolutely nothing. As William E. Carroll puts it succinctly, "It is still something—how else could 'it' fluctuate?" He stresses again the difference between "nothing" as used in creation and the "nothing" discussed in contemporary cosmology. Thus, we need to recognize that the "nothing" discussed by present-day cosmologists is not absolutely nothing. It still has a *causa materialis*. Those who claim that a "void" or "nothing" can be described mathematically with a wave function—which they consider the quantum gravity equivalent of the quantum vacuum in quantum field theory—seem to entirely miss the point that such a wave function is also something rather than nothing (see chapter 7).

When quantum cosmologists blithely characterize their vacuum fluctuation as being the scientific equivalent of *creatio ex nihilo*, they entirely misconstrue the discussion. When God created *ex nihilo*, He did not use some peculiar sort of stuff called *nihil* from which to make the universe. As John Polkinghorne puts it, "A quantum vacuum is not *nihil*, for it is structured by the laws of quantum mechanics and the equations of the quantum fields involved." The contention of these new theories is that the laws of physics would be sufficient to account for the origin and existence of the universe. If there is any metaphysical assumption lurking behind this view, it is that the mere existence of things needs no explanation. This view has rightly been caricatured by the Boston College philosopher Peter Kreeft as a magical "pop theory" that has things pop into existence without any cause. A Higgs boson, for instance, cannot just pop itself into existence; it must have a cause, because it does not and cannot have the power to make itself exist.

Most cosmologists refer to the Big Bang as a "singularity," that is, an ultimate boundary or edge, a "state of infinite density" where space-time has ceased. Thus it represents an outer limit of what we can know about the universe, since it is not possible to speculate, at least in the natural sciences, about conditions before or beyond the categories of space and time. Nevertheless, Stephen Hawking argues that the notion of an initial "singularity," which seems to require a temporal beginning of the universe, needs to be rejected. He denies the intelligibility of a "beginning" to the universe, since time itself emerged in the very early universe. So, according to Hawking, the universe does not have a boundary: "It is completely self-contained and not affected by anything outside itself. It would neither be created nor destroyed. It would just be." Then he concludes again that without an initial singularity there is nothing for a Creator to do. Apparently, Hawking identifies creation with a temporal beginning of the universe. William E. Carroll rightly concludes, "Thus, he thinks that by denying such a beginning he can deny creation."

But again, Big Bang cosmology, even with recent variations, neither supports nor detracts from the doctrine of creation, since cosmology studies change, whereas creation is not a change. Some have argued in response that an initial "singularity," outside the categories of space and time, points to a supernatural cause of the beginning of the universe. But the concept of creation does not need the support of any science, not even of Big Bang cosmology.

Before the Big Bang?

What are we to make then of the temporal order of things in creating the universe? Was the Big Bang "preceded" by creation?

Was creation the event that happened "before" the Big Bang took place, or even could take place?

Again, we need Aquinas for some clear distinctions. It is true that creation must come "first" before any events, even a Big Bang, can follow. But creation is not an event at all. Creation concerns the *origin* of the universe—its source of being—not its *beginning* in time. Creation must come first in the order of primacy, but not in the order of time. Creation is not some distant event; instead, it is the complete causing of the existence of everything that is—in the past, now, and in the future. Therefore, as Aquinas keeps insisting, creation is a subject for metaphysics and theology; it is not a subject for the natural sciences or cosmology. The doctrine of creation affirms that all that is, in whatever way or ways it is, depends upon God as a primary cause. Without the primary cause, there could not be any secondary causes. Creation is the radical causing of the whole existence of whatever exists—it is not a change at all. The natural sciences, on the other hand, have as their subject the world of changing things—from subatomic particles to bacteria to galaxies. Aquinas would point out that whenever there is a change, there must be something that changes.

True, the unfolding of the universe, starting with the Big Bang, is a process that plays out in time and can be studied by the physical sciences. Creation, on the other hand, cannot follow a timeline, as time itself is also a product of creation. Albert Einstein showed us that both time and space are part of the physical world, just as much as matter and energy. In point of fact, time can be manipulated in the laboratory. Dramatic time warps occur, for example, when subatomic particles are accelerated to near the speed of light, and black holes stretch time by an infinite amount.

Centuries ago, long before Einstein, Aquinas had already made it very clear that creation is not some chronological episode, located somewhere back in time, when he said, "God brought into being both the creature and time together," and, "Before the world, there was no time," and, "It is idle to look for time before creation, as if time can be found before time." In other words, our universe may have a beginning and a timeline, but creation itself does not have a beginning or a timeline. The discussion as to whether the universe has a *beginning* or not has no impact on the *origin* of the universe. William E. Carroll rightly remarks, "Were the universe to be without a beginning it still would have an origin, it still would be created."

So we cannot place creation at the beginning of time, since there is no time until time has been created; creating time "at a certain time" is just tough to do! God himself is timeless. Creation is not something that happened long ago in time, and neither is the Creator someone who did something in the distant past; the Creator does something at all times—by keeping a contingent world in existence. Whereas the universe may have a beginning and a timeline, creation itself does not have a beginning or a timeline; creation actually makes the beginning of the universe and its timeline possible. Creation creates chronology, but it is not a part of chronology. Therefore it does not make sense to ask what happened before the Big Bang, because there was no time yet until time had been created. William E. Carroll would stress again that we should never confuse temporal *beginnings* with metaphysical *origins*.

Creation is the ongoing complete causing of the existence of all that is. At this very moment, were God not causing all that is to exist, there would be nothing at all. In other words, God creates without taking any time to create—he creates eternally. In creating, God does not become a secondary cause. Creation is not a process with a beginning, a middle, and an end. It is simply a reality: the reality of the complete dependence of the universe on God's agency. God does not act as part of a process, nor does God initiate a process where there was none before. There is no "before" for God; there is no preexisting state from which God's action proceeds. In the words of philosopher Michael W. Tkacz, "God is totally and immediately present as Primary Cause to any and all processes in the universe."

As a consequence, creation is not a "onetime event," but it relates to the question of where this universe ultimately comes from; it does not come from the Big Bang, but it may have started with the Big Bang. Without creation, there could not be anything—no Big Bang, no gravity, no evolution, not even a timeline. Creation sets the "stage" for these and keeps this world in existence. The "rest of the story" would be something for science to tell—and science is definitely trying hard. This allows William E. Carroll to state, "We do not get closer to creation by getting closer to the Big Bang," because creation is not an event in the explanatory domain of cosmology—it is a metaphysical concept.

Thus, it does not make sense to ask what happened before the Big Bang. Curiously enough, Stephen Hawking is often quoted as saying that asking what happened before the Big Bang is like asking what lies north of the North Pole. Hawking certainly did not say this because he wished to express his belief in creation. Rather, he based this on the astrophysical model he developed in collaboration with Jim Hartle, in which the universe has no boundary in space-time. He believes that if we push back the expansion of the universe far enough into the past, space-time is reduced to a single point. The following analogy may explain this. When you are standing exactly at the North Pole, there is indeed no such thing as a direction called "north"; there is no boundary there—it is simply the point where all north-running lines meet and end. In a similar way, there is no such thing as "before" when you get to the point that marks the "pole" of space-time, according to Hawking.

There is some truth to this. The only way to have a scientific theory is on condition that the laws of physics hold everywhere, including at the beginning of the universe. If all physical theories are formulated in the context of space and time, it would not be possible to speculate, at least not in the natural sciences, about conditions before or beyond these categories. In that sense, there is nothing "before" the Big Bang. But this also holds on metaphysical grounds: without creation, there is nothing, not even time—and thus there is no "before." The Big Bang did not "create" time, any more than it "created" gravity, let alone the law of gravity. Only creation *ex nihilo* does this!

According to William E. Carroll, a mistake Hawking makes in his denial of creation is the old error—which Aquinas pointed out—of "thinking that *ex nihilo* necessarily means *post nihilum*." When Hawking says, "But if the universe is really completely

self-contained, having no boundary or edge, it would have neither beginning nor end," he thinks that because there is nothing
"before nothing"—and therefore, nothing "after nothing"—he is
entitled to also deny "out of nothing."

A Universe Without "Gaps"

Once the universe is in existence—through creation, that is—it
can further develop because of its own laws and its own entities,
without any interventions from outside the universe. Aquinas
teaches us that the creation of the universe depends on God, the
primary cause, but whatever happens inside the universe depends
on secondary causes. This distinction between primary cause and
secondary causes is vital in his philosophy—and vital for us.

Although Aquinas also makes a distinction between the coming into existence and the staying in existence—the latter he calls
more specifically preservation or conservation—in Aquinas's
view, preservation is no different from creation in the sense that
they *both* depend on God. Aquinas holds that everything other
than God gets its being from God. Put differently, any "thing" left
entirely to itself, wholly separated from the cause of its existence,
would cease to exist and be absolutely nothing. Whereas the Big
Bang theory offers us a scientific account of how a later state of
the physical world might have emerged from an earlier state, creation offers us a metaphysical account of where the material
world itself comes from (creation) and how it stays in existence
(conservation).

Many atheists and believers alike make the wrong assumption
that if we speak of divine action, we must be thinking of God as
simply one cause among many other causes in the universe.
Thus, scientific explanations are set in competition with divine
explanations. But again, in Aquinas's eyes, this is a serious mix-up.
Divine causation works at a level completely different from that
of secondary causation, and science can examine only the latter
(see chapter 3). For Aquinas, there is no conflict between the doctrine of creation and any physical theory. Theories in the natural
sciences account for change. Whether the changes described are
cosmological, physical, biological, or psychological, they remain

processes based on secondary causes. Creation, on the other hand, accounts for the existence of things, not changes in things, and for their total dependence on the primary cause.

This Thomistic distinction remains essential for avoiding the confusion that seems to be all around us. True, CERN's famous Large Hadron Collider may help unravel the "mystery" of the beginning of this universe, but certainly not the "mystery" of the creation or origin of this universe. These are two very different kinds of "mystery." If the Higgs boson is indeed the particle that could explain why there is mass in the universe, then a physical "mystery" may have been solved—but certainly not the "mystery" of creation, of creating something out of nothing and bringing it into being. When the physicist Leon Lederman called the Higgs boson "the God particle" in the title of his 1993 book, he was—deliberately perhaps—meddling with two kinds of mysteries.

God's creative power is exercised throughout the entire course of cosmic history, in whatever ways that history has unfolded. God creates a universe in which things have their own causal agency, their own true self-sufficiency—which makes for a nature that is open to scientific analysis. As William E. Carroll observes, "No explanation of cosmological processes, nor biological change for that matter, regardless of how radically random or contingent such an explanation claims to be, challenges the metaphysical account of creation, that is, of the dependence of the existence of all things upon God as cause." God is not a rival or contender for created causes, but rather the One who makes all secondary causes be their own causes.

Aquinas's distinction between change and creation should make us fully aware of the radical otherness or transcendence of God's agency. God's productive causality is unlike that of any natural cause. God is not a cause among other causes. God produces what He produces not only all at once without any process, but also without requiring anything preexisting or any preconditions whatsoever. God does not act as part of a process, nor does God initiate a process where there was none before. There is no "before" for God; there is no preexisting state from which God's action proceeds. God is totally and immediately present as primary cause to any and all processes as secondary causes.

If this is so, then there is no need for the primary cause to further interfere with secondary causes, since the latter work on their own. If God, the primary cause, had to interfere in the evolution of the universe, He would be downgraded to a secondary cause that works *inside* the universe in order to fill the gaps supposedly left behind by all the other secondary causes. Yet, even the famous physicist Isaac Newton gave in to this timeless temptation of having God keep a "divine foot" in the door, when he called upon God's active intervention to periodically reform the solar system from increasing irregularities, and to prevent the stars from falling in on one another, and perhaps even to prevent the amount of motion in the universe from decaying owing to viscosity and friction. Had he listened to Aquinas, he could have been aware that God does not have to make such interventions—and in fact, science would soon be able to explain them with the proper laws (which are God's laws anyway). Newton wrongly made the primary cause periodically intervene like a secondary cause.

Creatures, both animate and inanimate, are real causes of the wide array of changes that occur in the world, but God alone is the universal cause of being as such. God's causality is so different from the causality of creatures that there is no competition between the two—that is, we do not need to limit, as it were, God's causality to make room for the causality of creatures. God, the primary cause, causes creatures to be causes themselves—secondary causes, that is.

All these great distinctions and insights we owe to Aquinas. Let us conclude this section with one more quote from William E. Carroll: "Thomas Aquinas did not have the advantage of the Hubble Space Telescope, but in many ways he is able to see farther and more clearly than those who do."

To open the mind for further study:

Barr, Stephen M. *Modern Physics and Ancient Faith*. South Bend, IN: University of Notre Dame Press, 2006.

Carroll, William E., and Baldner, Steven E. *Aquinas on Creation.* Toronto: Pontifical Institute of Mediaeval Studies, 1997.

Craig, William Lane, and Smith, Quentin. *Theism, Atheism, and Big Bang Cosmology.* Oxford University Press, 1993.

7

Aquinas and Physics

Classical Physics

THE MATHEMATICAL is the first property of all physical things, so mathematics is, as Aquinas says, the science most connatural to man. Physics testifies to the truth of this statement. Physics provides us with tremendous information about physical things, but it is largely expressed in mathematical equations. How did that come about?

It started when René Descartes discovered a new method of doing mathematics. Mathematics studies quantity, so the new method looks at quantity as a logical system of symbols. Before Descartes, scientists focused on quantity itself—i.e., extension, being a property of physical things—and did not allow symbols to take a controlling role. After Descartes, it was Isaac Newton who successfully centered physics on a logical system that is easily put into two fundamental mathematical equations:

$F = ma$, where F is the net force applied, m is the mass of the body, and a is the body's acceleration.

$F = G \times ((m_1 \times m_2) / r^2)$, where F is the force between the masses, G is the gravitational constant, m_1 is the first mass, m_2 is the second mass, and r is the distance between the centers of the masses.

From then on, scientific thinking was no longer based on physical entities but on mental entities—no longer expressed in terms of things but in terms of symbols, no longer in terms of sensing but of thinking. Physics had become a matter of manipulating symbols in mathematical equations. Attention was now exclusively focused on the *causa formalis* of equations, without further consideration of their *causa materialis*. Since then, we seem to know things through equations rather than through the senses.

So the question arises: Where do these equations exist? For many, the answer seems to be: only in our minds. So the new idea is to start in our minds, in the non-material world, thus bypassing the material world of our bodies and what we sense through our senses. Since then we know the world through equations. Thus, we have lost direct contact with reality, with the world of objectivity—which clearly violates the basics of Aquinas's epistemology (see chapter 4). Mathematical structure is of itself a mere abstraction, and there must be some concrete reality that *has* the structure. Albert Einstein, for one, always resented this trend of "mathematicalization" in physics. He did not want to be a slave to mathematics. For instance, after he had studied Fr. Lemaître's 1927 paper intensely, he told the priest, "Your mathematics is perfect, but your physics is abominable." Einstein would one day take back those words, but his point was that mathematics does not have the last word. Bertrand Russell once said, "Physics is mathematical not because we know so much about the physical world, but because we know so little."

Jacques Maritain, a philosopher in the Aquinas tradition, ranks the alliance of physics with mathematics as one of the great discoveries of modern times—and rightly so. He calls physics "materially physical and formally mathematical." The secret is in the word "and." Although physics both starts and ends in the physical reality, it submits the measurements it has drawn from the physical world to the rule of mathematics—that is, for the most part, it attempts to explain physical things insofar as they can be described mathematically. Hence, modern physics by its very methods leaves much of reality behind. One could say that in physics the *causa formalis* of equations has more or less displaced the role of the *causa materialis*. Alfred North Whitehead called this the "fallacy of misplaced concreteness"—a fallacy that we commit when we mistake our abstractions for concrete realities. Niels Bohr once famously acknowledged, "If we want to say anything at all about nature—and what else does science try to do?—we must somehow pass from mathematical to everyday language."

As an illustration of what this means, consider the following example. To understand the operation of a wheel, a physicist might think of it as a circle and do calculations and get results about how a wheel behaves. However, if we then forgot all the realities that our initial abstraction has left behind and proceeded to conclude that a wheel is nothing but a circle, we would quickly draw seriously erroneous conclusions. What physics gives us is a description of the mathematical structure of physical reality. It ignores or neglects any aspect of reality that cannot be captured via its exclusively quantitative methods. So when something does not show up in the description physics gives us, we should not conclude that it is not there in the physical world. Using exclusively mathematical language will necessarily leave out any aspect of physical reality that is not reducible to the quantitative. Since physics deals with abstractions from concrete reality—not concrete reality itself—it does not give us anything close to a complete description of material reality. Isaac Newton once quipped, "Gravitation is not responsible for people falling in love."

In addition, the notion of idealization obviously affects the way we learn and teach physics in schools and colleges. Beginning students of physics quickly become acquainted with idealizations such as the notion of a frictionless surface, and with the fact that laws such as Newton's law of gravitation mathematically describe the behavior of bodies only in the situation where no interfering forces are acting on them—a situation that never actually holds. They learn equations but gain hardly any knowledge of the realities behind them. Michael Augros mentions his experience of how his physics teacher in high school explained the difference between *mass* and *weight* with the question, "Would you rather lift my car or push it?" That's how he learned that mass resists your push, and weight resists your lift. That step in understanding seems to be necessary before the equations begin.

Moreover, physicists draw their conclusions from highly specialized experiments conducted under rather artificial conditions. As a consequence, one cannot translate physics, which is now fundamentally mathematical, into layman's language, without being conscious of the implicit philosophical assumptions that are necessary in order to do the translation. Mathematical structure by itself is a mere abstraction; it cannot be all there is, because structure presupposes something concrete that *has* the structure.

Nowadays, to use another example, we are taught at an early age the current version of centuries-old atomism—that all things are composed of atoms, and that atoms are the building blocks of all matter. This modern teaching holds that the nature of a human being, for instance, is strictly material, nothing more than matter and energy expressed mathematically. Since we "know" about atoms and that we are composed of atoms, it seems reasonable to conclude that we are strictly a collection of atoms. Aquinas, however, would not buy into this line of reasoning. Anthony Rizzi—a physicist and philosopher working in the tradition of Aquinas—discusses this issue extensively. One of his examples is exactly the above issue: what is an atom? We are taught that an atom is composed of electrons and a nucleus. The electron is point-like, and most of the mass of the atom is in the nucleus of the atom. If the nucleus were the size of a basketball, the "edge" of the atom would be two miles away.

It is thus said and believed that the atom is filled with mostly empty space—which made a student say during an exam that atoms mostly consist of air! If an atom is basically made up mostly of empty space, though, imagine the notion that an object such as the human body is actually a collection of a huge number (10^{28}) of atoms. In any given atom, the nucleus contains 99.9 percent of the mass of the entire atom. But its diameter is only $1/100,000$ of the surrounding electron cloud. Given that the size of the atom is determined by the orbit of the outermost electron (for our purposes), the atom is thus 99.9999999999 percent open space. We would end up being mostly empty—or "air" in the minds of some.

What are we to make of this? Having noted that the first modern ideas about the existence of atoms were deduced from purely mathematical observations, Rizzi goes on to show that not one of us has ever seen an atom, but we know from contemporary physical theory that the kind of electromagnetic interaction recorded between electrons seems to be in effect throughout the whole atom at various intensities and moments, indicating that between the nucleus and its electrons there is some "intangible thing" that fills the intervening "empty" space and which is the cause of any observed fluctuations and changes. If so, the atom is *not* filled with mostly empty space. Rizzi connects this idea with Aquinas's principle of "no action at a distance." Let us find out what that principle means.

Aquinas declared emphatically that "a body cannot act where it is not." This means that an object cannot be moved, changed, or otherwise affected without being physically touched. So this could be a problem for interactions between electrons and protons, which seem so far apart—not to mention interactions between celestial bodies. Forces act at a distance, but how do they act at a distance with no "physical" connections between them? Aquinas denies that there is such a thing as action at a distance (*actio in distans*). Although Aquinas acknowledges there are apparent violations of this principle—such as the heating of the earth by the sun—he insists that in all such cases there must be a medium of transmission of the action, even though the form the action takes in the medium may be very different from its effect on the object where the action terminates. Later on, Einstein more or less joined Aquinas's view when he called action at a distance a "spooky" idea.

However, this Thomistic rejection of action at a distance came under serious attack when Isaac Newton introduced his law of gravitation, which asserts that the heavenly bodies act on one another across immense intervals of space. Does this mutual action depend on the existence of some third thing, some medium of communication, occupying the space between the heavenly bodies—or do the bodies act on each other immediately, without the intervention of anything else? Newton did not really think in terms of action at a distance. He stated, "That gravity should be innate, inherent, and essential to matter, so that one body can act upon another at a distance, through a vacuum, without the mediation of anything else, . . . is to me so great an absurdity, that I believe no man who has in philosophical matters a competent faculty of thinking can ever fall into it." In connection with light, Newton in his *Opticks* would try to persuade those who opposed action at a distance by appealing to the idea of "ether" through which rays of light could propagate. Physics theories of the late nineteenth century assumed that just as surface water waves must have a supporting "medium" to move across water and audible sound requires a medium to transmit its wave motions in air or water, so light must also require a medium to transmit its wave motions. Because light can travel through a vacuum, it was assumed that even a vacuum must be filled with ether.

The idea of ether and other media was not well received by most physicists at the time. They preferred to commit themselves to "sweeping cobwebs off the sky," as they described it. The new motto was that physicists should investigate the forces with which bodies act on each other in the first place—mathematically, that is—before attempting to explain how those forces are transmitted. This motto was in line with the growing "mathematicalization" trend in physics: as long as the equations work, so the reasoning goes, one should not worry about the mechanisms behind them. As a consequence, electromagnetic forces, for instance, can be rationalized as action at a distance expressed in mathematical functions and equations. But the question remains what "it" is that acts according to those equations.

It is not surprising that the tide would eventually turn. The exclusive search for mathematical equations could no longer suppress the intuitive need for an anchor in reality—for a *causa materialis*. Because of this need, action at a distance became more and more unpopular around the middle of the nineteenth century, when scientists returned to Aquinas's view that bodies cannot act where they are not; there had to be a medium of transmission of the action—or at least some hidden variable.

How could this be true of electric and magnetic forces, for instance, since there is no direct contact between the two charges? One of the first scientists who more or less revived the theory of action through medium was Michael Faraday. Faraday assumed an invisible medium, even in a vacuum, that would transmit the Coulomb force. One of his favorite demonstrations was showing magnetic field lines—which Faraday called "lines of force"—by sprinkling iron filings onto a sheet of paper held over a bar magnet. The filings align themselves within the magnetic field, thus showing the pattern normally invisible to us. His contemporary, James Maxwell, tended in the same direction when he introduced the concept of the electromagnetic field comparable to the force lines that Faraday had described.

Physicists nowadays consider the medium of electromagnetism not as material that fills the space but the space, or field, itself. The concept of *field* has become an alternative way of dealing with action at a distance. Every electrically charged object creates an electric field in space around it. Another object, placed in the field, will then "feel" the force exerted on it by the field, even though it could be far away from the actual source of the field. This is of course a "classical" explanation; in quantum physics, particles and fields are equivalent. So we could say in Thomistic terms that it is the nature of an electron, for instance, that its trajectory is changed by the presence of an electric field. The potential for this change in trajectory, when this particular field is present, describes a potency in the nature of the electron. A potency can be actualized only by something already actual, which could be something internal to the thing itself, or something external. It could be a state of affairs, a tension in the energy field, or almost anything—whatever it is that explains the changes.

Skeptics, of course, may always counter that it is anyone's guess what a "field" is, and whether it really exists. When field theory views an electron as a "ripple" or wave of a field, the question remains whether this is indeed so—and even if it is, whether a field is perhaps only a mathematical construct. When Feynman diagrams are used to "depict" field theory, for instance, these diagrams are merely taken as pictorial representations of the mathematical expressions governing the behavior of subatomic particles. When asked what electricity is, physicists are, of course, apt to answer that electricity is a field, like gravitation. But still the question can be raised: What is a field? Stanley Jaki is right when he says, "If we answer that a field is an oscillation, the answer begs the question: what is it that oscillates?" The Nobel laureate Hendrik Lorentz commented that "whether there is an aether or not, electromagnetic fields certainly exist, and so also does the energy of the electrical oscillations. . . . [I]f we do not like the name of 'aether,' we must use another word as a peg to hang all these things upon."

Something similar can be said about gravity. According to the general theory of relativity, gravity is a phenomenon resulting from the curvature of space-time. Massive bodies attract each other by distorting space-time via their mass rather than by action at a distance. Just as a change in an electromagnetic field propagates as an electromagnetic wave and exerts electromagnetism, so a change in gravitational field propagates as a gravitational wave and exerts gravity. The outcome is that both gravitation and electromagnetism—which were once thought to be occult actions at a distance—can also be explained as action through medium. Even in quantum theory, it could be claimed that a vacuum is not really vacant but a fluctuating field of particles that can transmit electromagnetic waves.

Consequently, we could say that realism is still important in physics, in spite of all mathematical appearances. Physics, as it is practiced today according to Rizzi, is indeed formally mathematical, but that does not take away from the fact that it is materially physical. We could also demonstrate this with the concept of "simultaneity" in Einstein's theory of relativity. Jacques Maritain has pointed out the kind of metaphysical confusion that results if we confuse the findings of physics with the ontological nature of the world. Einstein's simultaneity, which he demonstrates to be relative to a specific frame of reference, is not the same as real simultaneity in the philosophical sense. We may construct a situation, as Einstein does with his famous example of the observer on the train and the observer outside the train, both trying to decide if two events are simultaneous. But this is simultaneity as measured from a certain frame of reference, which may be the only thing that a physicist is interested in, and it does not have any ontological content despite the fact that Einstein implied that it did. However, from a philosophical point of view, two events are either simultaneous or they are not. They either happen at the same instant or they do not. They cannot both happen and not happen at the same moment, but they depend on what their frames of reference are. So what is at stake in this debate is the very existence of matter and the objectivity of things.

It would be interesting to mention what the Nobel laureate Robert B. Laughlin has to say about ether in contemporary theoretical physics:

> Relativity actually says nothing about the existence or non-existence of matter pervading the universe, only that any such matter must have relativistic symmetry. . . . It turns out that such matter exists. . . . Subsequent studies with large particle accelerators have now led us to understand that space is more like a piece of window glass than ideal Newtonian emptiness. It is filled with 'stuff' that is normally transparent but can be made visible by hitting it sufficiently hard to knock out a part. The modern concept of the vacuum of space, confirmed every day by experiment, is a relativistic ether. But we do not call it this because it is taboo.

So there might still be room for a medium with physical properties filling "empty" space, some kind of "ether," enabling the physical processes we observe. The Nobel laureate Paul Dirac wrote in 1951, "If one examines the question in the light of present-day knowledge, one finds that the Aether is no longer ruled out by relativity, and good reasons can now be advanced for postulating an Aether." Those who say that the famous Michelson–Morley experiment has proved the non-existence of ether should realize this experiment does not prove that ether does not exist, only that it has not been detected. Einstein knew that special relativity could be formulated in terms of ether, but he reasoned it was mathematically simpler not to posit its existence.

To wrap up this discussion, it may be worthwhile to delve into a more basic ontological aspect of physics. Since it seems that anything might ultimately change into anything else, Aristotle and Aquinas postulated that there is an ultimate stuff that underlies the radical potency of everything to turn into anything else. Since Aristotle calls whatever is the bearer of potency the "matter" in any change, this ultimate stuff is called "prime matter." Prime matter, in its own theoretical self, is without any determination but is mere potentiality as such. It exists only in actual determinate things, as the radical potency to undergo limitless changes. Prime matter is only and always found with some substantial form that gives it determination. Yet, although it never exists in and of itself, prime matter is real; it is a real principle of change. It is the real potency that every material thing has in order to undergo an indefinite amount of change.

The question is, of course, if this metaphysical Thomistic view has not been superseded by developments in modern physics. Modern nuclear physicists tell us that the matter of everything can ultimately and theoretically be converted into energy, and energy can similarly be converted into matter—in equation, $E = mc^2$. Nevertheless, there still seems to be some principle that underlies each of these two ways of being physical but cannot exist without being one or the other, matter or energy. Thus, it seems that we still have a metaphysical need for the notion of what Aquinas called "prime matter."

Quantum Physics

Quantum mechanics—also known as quantum physics or quantum theory—provides a mathematical description of much of the dual particle-like and wave-like behavior and interactions of energy and matter. Some claim that Aquinas's epistemology, which embraces a realism that affirms the existence of the objective world and our ability to know it, has become outdated and has forever been defeated by the quantum physicist Niels Bohr and his school—in spite of objections made by some giant opponents. Why do so many believe that Aquinas is outdated in this respect?

According to Werner Heisenberg's "principle of *uncertainty*," it is impossible to determine simultaneously the values of position and momentum with any great degree of certainty; the more precisely one property is known, the less precisely the other can be known. Some objects just have multiple properties that appear to be contradictory. Sometimes it is possible to switch back and forth between different views of an object to observe these properties, but in principle, it is impossible to view both at the same time. This phenomenon is known even in classical physics: it is impossible for us to know the exact frequencies in a sound wave at an exact moment in time.

Most quantum physicists will accept this account. The question, though, is how to interpret this phenomenon of "uncertainty." It is striking that there are at least seventeen different interpretations of quantum mechanics. In Niels Bohr's interpretation, which is called the "principle of *indeterminacy*," these values are in essence undetermined until we measure one of them. He stresses "the impossibility of any sharp separation between the behavior of atomic objects [i.e., objects governed by quantum mechanics] and the interaction with the measuring instruments which serve to define the conditions under which the phenomena appear." Light, for example, behaves either as a wave or as a stream of particles depending on our experimental setup, but not only can we never observe both quantities at the same time, they also are assumed to have no precise values until measured. Therefore, the behavior of atoms and electrons can presumably no longer be predicted until determined by a measuring device, says Bohr. He sees the world of physics as ultimately undetermined.

Bohr was able to manage a "well-oiled" public relations campaign for his interpretation and developed a powerful school of followers, the Copenhagen school. Nevertheless, he also had powerful opponents such as Albert Einstein, Max Planck, David Bohm, and Erwin Schrödinger—to name just a few. Which side is right? Scientific debates should never be decided by majority vote, of course. Fans often just echo what they have learned from their master. What we need here is a scientific assessment—although it is not quite clear whether we are dealing with a scientific or rather a metaphysical disagreement. It is definitely a search for truth—why argue anyway if truth does not matter?

Some claim that the Copenhagen interpretation is actually an attempt to do metaphysics under the guise of physics, all the while sneering cynically at those who state that metaphysics is more properly a branch of philosophy than of science. What happens easily in this discussion is that certain philosophical assumptions are first "read into" quantum mechanics and then "read out" again. Edward Feser summarizes this as follows: "It is the metaphysical background assumptions we bring to bear on quantum mechanics that determine how we interpret it."

Before we continue, a few more general comments or critical remarks should be made. Ironically, Bohr and his Copenhagen school try to give us a causal explanation of the alleged fact that causal explanations are no longer possible in their view. They think that we do not know because we cannot know; they maintain that it is impossible to regard objects governed by quantum mechanics as having intrinsic properties independent of determination with a measuring device. The problem is, though, that our perceptual experiences give us knowledge of the external physical world only because they are *causally* related to that world. To deny causality in the name of science would therefore be to undermine the very empirical foundations of science. How could we ever account for our knowledge of the world that physics tells us about if we have no causal contact with it at all?

Michael Augros uses a good example to make this point. Let us assume that the infamous double-slit experiment demonstrates the inadequacy of either the particle model or the wave model for electrons. Since it is not possible to track the electrons at every moment along their path without making them go through just one slit, so that no interference pattern arises, how do we know the interference pattern has anything to do with the electrons at all? We don't observe the electrons continuously from their emission to their striking the screen. We assume that when two natural phenomena are such that one always follows after the other, and there is nothing that is causing both of them, then the first of them is causing the second. So the firing of electrons and the interference pattern must be connected as cause and effect.

Another problem with Bohr's interpretation is that quantum physics tells us something about the dispositional features of fundamental particles—how they can behave. Well, "dispositionality" is a causal notion. The "power" of an acid to dissolve a metal, for instance, is a dispositional property. Newton's laws, to use another example, attribute dispositional behavior to bodies; they state that the bodies would manifest certain behavior in the absence of disturbing factors or forces. Some have gone as far as denying dispositional features of fundamental particles; they claim that quantum mechanics has undermined classical logic, especially the law of excluded middle, which states that for any proposition, either that proposition is true, or its negation is true. It is hard to defend such claims. The laws of quantum physics—like all other laws of physics—are merely descriptive. They tell us what happens, but they do not tell us why it happens that way. The status of causality as such is something about which the laws of quantum physics themselves are completely silent. The causality of electromagnetism, gravitation, mass, etc. is, strictly speaking, irrelevant to the laws. Yet causality is key.

Furthermore, it could be argued that it is logically impossible to prove that something has no cause at all. Causality can never be conclusively defeated by experiments, since causality is the very foundation of experiments and of the way science works. The famous tool of falsification, for instance, is in and of itself based on the assumption of causality and order: scientific evidence could never refute a scientific hypothesis if there were no order and causality in this universe. Even Popper himself realized that falsificationism is not itself a scientific thesis but a meta-level claim about science. Without the assumption of order, there just could not be any falsifying evidence. It is a principle that cannot coherently be denied. So counterevidence does allow us to falsify theories, but not the principle of falsification itself. The physical order we observe in this world appears to be amazingly "consistent," so why would it be different when it comes to quantum theory? Those who claim there is a difference owe us at least an explanation regarding why we should draw the line where they say we should, and how there could be such a line.

No wonder the quantum physicist David Bohm gives us a pretty sarcastic, yet rather accurate, description of the Copenhagen interpretation of quantum mechanics with the following remarks. It is supposed to be one of its virtues that it is entirely random and statistical, Bohm says, and hence there is no explanation for the phenomenon of uncertainty in quantum mechanics. Then he goes on, it has no explanation of time, of how one moment becomes another. That is, quantum mechanics is a theory of one moment, of one measurement, and there is a statistical probability of getting a certain result. Then, says Bohm, you drop whatever you have done and start out with the next measurement, and apply statistics again. It does not explain how you get from one measurement to the other, or in fact why or how any measurement produces the result that it does. It says the equation will give you the probability, and that's all there is to it. Thus, Bohm proposed separating wave and particle: the particle is what we see; the wave is a "pilot" wave, carrying information about the environment and manifesting itself solely by its "guidance" of the particle. That's Bohm's view of the issue, but it is strongly disputed. Let's leave it at that.

Aquinas would probably have been pleased at the sound philosophical instincts that moved Bohm to avoid philosophical indeterminism as a direct consequence of quantum theory, and embrace instead a realism that affirms the objectivity of the world and our ability to know it—for without these, science would collapse. Working in the Aquinas tradition, Jacques Maritain traces our inability to know the precise position and velocity of a particle back to the disturbances our measurements create. Whether this explanation is true or not, he is right in saying that it is not the place of physics to elevate this indeterminacy to a philosophical conclusion that speaks of the indeterminacy of nature itself. Physics has the right, of course, to create a nondeterministic view of microphysics and to look at quantum waves as waves of probability, as long as it doesn't give these constructs a philosophical interpretation. In Bohr's interpretation, however, we seem to have lost contact with reality and causality. Bohr is more or less saying that reality does not exist when we are not observing it. And with regard to causality, his Copenhagen school will claim that individual quantum events are "radically uncaused" and "radically undetermined."

Let us analyze claims like these a bit further for one particular case, radioactive decay. Take, for instance, an unstable radium atom such as Ra^{88} that may decay, without outside interference, by α-decay into the radon atom Rn^{86}. Even though the half-life of this radioactive element can be determined (5.76 years), nothing determines when one particular atom will disintegrate—even though we can register the individual decay event on a Geiger counter. The decay of any particular atom is therefore literally considered uncaused by the Copenhagen school—a case of physics turned metaphysics. Would this be the end of Aquinas's metaphysics?

We discussed already that metaphysical issues can hardly ever, perhaps even never, be settled by physical facts. Aquinas would certainly accept Bohr's physical data, but not his metaphysical interpretation. Physics makes generalizations, metaphysics offers universal principles. Let's look at the case of radioactive decay again, but this time from the perspective of Aquinas's metaphysical view of causality. No one would deny that the particle came to be out of the decay of the atom, but at the moment it came to be, it did not have and was not able to have its own ground of being in itself. But then it must have its ground outside itself, which is the very notion of being caused. Aquinas takes the view that a substance can manifest certain dispositions in a "spontaneous" way in the sense that these manifestations simply follow from its nature or substantial form.

Edward Feser explains this, in the footsteps of Aquinas, by stating that the decay in question is "spontaneous" in the sense that, given the nature or substantial form of Ra^{88}, there is a certain probability that it will decay in the next minute. Probability is not denial of causality; the idea is that certain causes change the probability of their effects. This probability is not unintelligible but rather grounded in what it is to be Ra^{88}. The decay thus has a cause in the sense that it has a *formal* cause in the nature (or substantial form) of the particular Ra^{88} atom, and it has an *efficient* cause in whatever it was that originally generated that Ra^{88} atom. The particle, given off by the decay of the atom, is a being that is subject to change, and that does not have to be what it is. As Aquinas puts it, "Every contingent being has a ground other than itself, exterior to itself, that is to say an efficient cause." But the efficient cause is just whatever generated the substance and thus gave it the substantial form that accounts for its natural change.

Even if it is claimed that decay phenomena are incompatible with deterministic causality, it definitely does not follow that there is no causality at all in such cases. Even atomic decay requires some kind of cause, otherwise there would be no reason the decay happened at that time rather than some other time. All that would follow is that the causality is not deterministic but probabilistic. In the case of radioactive decay, we might say that the atom had the capacity to decay—the potency to release the particle—but this capacity cannot reduce itself to act. If it could, it would be at once in act and in potency. Aquinas's principle of causality states that any potential, if actualized, must be actualized by something already actual. Otherwise it would give itself the very being it does not have. That would amount to saying that being somehow comes out of nothingness—something Peter Kreeft rightly calls the "pop theory," with virtual particles constantly popping in and out of existence. Even if the sudden appearance of virtual particles can be regarded as nothing more than the fluctuations of some underlying quantum field, these fluctuations are changes, so they still require a cause. Even the claim that all matter spontaneously emerges, without a cause, from a "nonlocal field of infinite potentiality," ignores the fact that "spontaneity" is not the same thing as "being uncaused."

Some physicists such as Geoffrey Chew have tried another strategy to make the universe pull itself into existence by its own bootstraps. They maintain that particles are made out of other particles by a force holding them together, and that this force is itself due to the exchange of particles between particles. This gives particles a double role: as carriers of force and as consequences of force. This amounts to identifying carrier with consequence, which contradicts the classical philosophical and logical rule that cause and effect must be distinct from each other.

Werner Heisenberg at least realized there was a problem with the Copenhagen interpretation. Heisenberg developed a realist view of the microworld that is based on the Aristotelian concept of potency. Some call him the last (quantum) physicist with a philosophical background. In his view, the inhabitants of the quantum world possess tendencies to exist, or ranges of potentialities, which have a strange kind of reality somewhere between possibility and actuality. He recognized that there is, in addition to what is actual on the one hand, and sheer nothingness on the other, a middle ground of potentiality, such that change is the actualization of a potentiality. It was this idea that made Heisenberg maintain that there are two ontological domains in the discourse of physicists. There supposedly is a gap between the two domains, and physicists manage to bridge it by a measurement process.

Aquinas's response to this would be that potency cannot exist except in relationship to act. There can be no potency floating around by itself. It is entirely possible that the inhabitants of the quantum world possess more potency than other beings, but their potency must be anchored in *act*, that is, in an actual being with a determinate nature, and therefore their potency is of a very definite and definitive kind. So Heisenberg's potency theory does not really create any cause as such. In response to the question of what the actuality is that is actualizing this potentiality, Heisenberg thought it was actualized by the act of observation. This is where physics ends and metaphysics begins.

Where does this leave us in the discussion regarding quantum mechanics and the principle of indeterminacy? The microworld may indeed seem strange in the sense that it can be neither perceived nor imagined, but it is not "quantum strange," as it is commonly thought to be. For example, it is by no means the case that the electron is sometimes a particle and sometimes a wave, or that it is somehow particle and wave at once, or that it "jumps" erratically from point to point, and so on. It is fully acceptable that we cannot know an exact energy at an exact time with infinite precision—but this does not mean that energy is appearing and disappearing within a system if we look at sufficiently short time intervals. What gives us the right to claim that if a physical object is not being observed, it is not really there? How can a radical lack of causality give rise to a world pervaded by causality? The "elusive" particles of quantum mechanics are part of what *is*. It is because they enable us to make sense of the world we live in that we believe in them.

Those who still want to reject the principle of causality should at least come up with an alternative metaphysical framework in which the rejection of the principle of causality is defensible, and within which these critics might embed their favored interpretation of quantum mechanics. Even what is considered a "standard" interpretation of quantum mechanics is still an interpretation of scientific observations. Its empirical claims float on an ocean of metaphysics. Dismissing the principle of causality is so far-reaching in its metaphysical implications that one ought to have an alternative metaphysical system before drawing such a conclusion. As we discussed earlier, causality is not based on a generalization that has been confirmed numerous times, but rather it is a universal principle that makes sensorial experiences *intelligible* for the human mind. Without such a principle, nothing would be intelligible anymore.

The discussion can probably be best summarized in Stanley Jaki's statement that the uncertainty principle is an epistemological, not ontological, statement. When physicists make statements about the nature of physical law, or causality, or the role of the observer in physical systems, they are really doing metaphysics rather than physics. Edward Feser is right when he says that quantum mechanics merely describes the behavior of a system; it tells us nothing about why the system behaves that way. It describes a particular state without describing its cause, but we cannot conclude from this that quantum mechanics shows us that such and such a state has no cause at all. All it does is place a limit on how much information we can simultaneously know about, say, the position and momentum of a particle, as such knowledge depends on the frame of reference we choose. But this does not actually mean that the particle lacks both a definite position and a definite momentum—only that it is impossible to know anything about both at the same time without a specific frame of reference. To assert that we cannot measure or otherwise know a precise position for a particle whose momentum is exactly known is an epistemological statement. On the other hand, to declare that this means that the particle does not actually have a precise position is an ontological and metaphysical statement, and it is an unproved —and unprovable—declaration at that.

Does this mean that there is no place left for chance in physics? Certainly not. Defending causality is entirely compatible with a view of the world in which probability plays a role. In Aquinas's view, chance is intricately connected with causality. Chance is only intelligible in terms of the order that it lacks; a previous order must exist before any chance event can even occur. If there were no order, there could be no chance, because chance needs the order of preexisting causes coming together "by coincidence" to produce unexpected results. When events occur "by chance," it is not because events are uncaused or because we cannot trace their causes, but because so many causal chains independent of each other intersect. There is nothing in any chain of events that is uncaused, but the intersection of certain chains does not have a cause in the usual sense of the term. Chance comes about because of the genuine causality that things exercise.

So it is not so much chance that is in dispute as indeterminacy. No wonder Einstein spent the last four decades of his life in a quest to restore "order" to physics. He realized that the concepts of order and causality do not come from science but are principles from philosophy and metaphysics that actually enable science. We are able to grasp and comprehend the world thanks, to a large extent, to our intellect and the observed order and causality of the world. The order we perceive is not a man-generated artifact. Paul Dirac said at a conference in 1979, "I think that it is very likely, or at any rate quite possible, that in the long run Einstein will turn out to be correct even though for the time being physicists have to accept the Bohr probability interpretation especially if they have examinations in front of them." Aquinas would most likely also defend Einstein, who so clearly realized that the physical sciences describe a reality independent of us as observers. Nonetheless, the indeterminacy debate remains very much alive in quantum physics, and it is still for many… well, indeterminate.

To open the mind for further study:

Arraj, James. *The Mystery of Matter*. Chiloquin, OR: Inner Growth Books, 1996.

Rizzi, Anthony. *The Science before Science*. Baton Rouge, LA: IAP Press, 2004.

Wallace, William A. *Modeling of Nature*. Washington, DC: Catholic University of America Press, 1996.

8

Aquinas and Genetics

GENETICS seems to be a perfect candidate for the fivefold causality of Aquinas's philosophy (see chapter 3). His analysis may help us gain a much better understanding of the role of DNA in genetics. Let us analyze each type of causality in more detail.

DNA's Causa Materialis

Thanks to some geneticists after him, Gregor Mendel has been heralded as "the father of genetics." The laws of genetics taught in high schools and colleges usually begin with what is called Mendel's laws. We therefore automatically assume that Mendel was talking about genes, about some kind of material entities that organisms transmit to the next generation—the *causa materialis* of genetics, so to speak. But that assumption is somewhat questionable. Although he uses sometimes the word "elements," his elements were most likely merely hypothetical constructs devised to systematically render the distribution of observable characters in inheritance. One of the reasons for thinking his elements were not concrete particles is the fact that Mendel represents constant forms—which we would now call homozygotes—with just *one* letter (*A* or *a* instead of *AA* or *aa*). Hybrids, on the other hand—which we would now call heterozygotes—he did express in our "modern" notation using *two* letters (*Aa*). However, in Mendel's view, an *Aa* organism is not a heterozygote but a hybrid. A hybrid is a mixture of two pure types and carries two different "elements" from each type. Even germ cells he called "of form A." There are also other indications that Mendel did not seem to be interested in the material structure of these elements.

For almost thirty-five years, Mendel's findings escaped notice, until other geneticists such as Hugo de Vries in Holland, Erich von Tschermak in Austria, Carl Correns in Germany, and William Bateson in England found similar data. When they came across Mendel's original paper from 1866, his work helped them interpret their own data better. Only one of them, Hugo de Vries, had previously been concerned with the material basis of inheritance. Most pioneer geneticists were not that far yet. What Mendel had referred to as "elements" and Bateson as "factors" were named "genes" by Johanssen, but they were basically more accounting or calculating units than material entities.

Further research revealed that two different genes (say, AaBb) did not always segregate independently from each other during hereditary transmission, but could be transmitted together (say, Ab but not AB). Bateson came up with explanations in terms of "coupling," or its opposite, "repulsion." Extensive tables of coupling ratios and repulsion ratios were drawn up—great for predictions but useless for explanations. It was more of a mathematical approach similar to what we saw in physics.

Soon, however, the need for a material basis became more pressing than ever. It had already been noticed by the geneticist Walter Sutton that genes always occur in pairs and that chromosomes also occur in pairs. Was this mere coincidence? Or could it be that genes and chromosomes are connected, and that genes are actually located in chromosomes? The call for a *causa materialis* was becoming louder than ever. If there is a connection between genes and chromosomes, then there must be many different genes per chromosome, as there are more genes than chromosomes. If so, it makes more sense that genes located on the same chromosome cannot separate independently but must be "coupled" or "linked," whereas genes located on different chromosomes can still separate independently of each other. At last, a physical, material connection had been made.

Yet, acceptance of chromosomes as material carriers of genes remained controversial. The leading geneticist Thomas Hunt Morgan fervently rejected the chromosome theory of heredity, but then he suddenly embraced it wholeheartedly in his classic 1910 paper in the journal *Science*. At last, Mendel's hypothetical elements had found a material basis. The chromosome theory could at least explain why the gene model works. Morgan's conception of the gene was now unequivocally material. Soon Morgan would develop chromosome "maps" representing the genes as lying in a line—"like beads on a string," as he put it. But the *causa materialis* of these "beads," the genes themselves, remained unclear and had to go through a much longer series of steps that would eventually lead to the discovery of DNA by Watson and Crick in 1953. Since then, our understanding of the material basis of the gene has gone through a fast-paced growth process.

Since the discovery of DNA, the atomistic conception of "beads on a string" has turned out to be too simplistic. The boundaries of a gene have become rather fuzzy, but a classical definition states that a gene is a unit of heredity that regulates a specific trait, feature, or characteristic of an organism. So it is understood to be a material entity. So what is it then that these genes carry? The simplest answer is DNA. A molecule of DNA (deoxyribonucleic acid) is composed of building blocks called nucleotides, each of which is itself composed of a five-carbon sugar bonded to a phosphate group and a nitrogenous base.

For the hungry minds among you (otherwise skip this paragraph), here are some more details. There are four kinds of nucleotides in DNA, which differ from one another in their nitrogenous bases: adenine (A) and guanine (G) are double-ring structures, whereas cytosine (C) and thymine (T) are single-ring structures. In a DNA molecule the nucleotides are arranged in sequence, held together by covalent bonds between the sugar of one nucleotide and the phosphate group of the next nucleotide beyond it; the nitrogenous bases are arranged as side groups off the chains. DNA molecules ordinarily exist as double-chain structures—comparable to a zipper—with the two chains held together by hydrogen bonds between their nitrogenous bases; such bonding can occur only between C and G (C–G bonds) or between T and A (T–A bonds). Finally, the ladder-like double-chain molecule is coiled into a double helix.

Thanks to the Human Genome Project, we currently know more details of the human DNA sequence. This achievement has caused quite a stir. It has made many people think—rather unjustifiably, of course—that DNA holds the script for a person's entire life. The new genomics has now become our latest crystal ball. Not surprisingly, the "arcane" idea of what Aquinas called *substance* seems to have gone out the window. From now on, it looks like human DNA determines the real nature of a human being—instead of some seemingly strange idea such as substance or essence. Let us find out if such a conclusion is warranted.

Those who declare DNA to be the fundamental reality of human beings and the prime building block of a human being would still need to explain the parts of DNA in order to explain DNA. Atoms might be a good candidate, but as the aerospace engineer S. M. Miranda remarks, atoms are composed of sub-atomic particles, which also demand explanation. These particles are in turn made of sub-subparticles, and so on and so on, until we arrive at some particle that is supposed to be the fundamental reality of a human being—the one thing that makes that human being real. However, even if we were to stop our subatomic chain at such a particle, we would still have to explain where that particle derives its "reality" from, which makes for an endless regress, unless we admit that this particle has no explanation for itself and must be an ultimate substance with accidents—a fundamental reality that has accidents such as mass, quality, and quantity; otherwise, we would not know where the quantity, quality, position, posture, etc. of the bearer of this DNA, such as a human being, come from.

Instead of seeking an endless series of sub-sub-explanations, why don't we just simply state instead that a human being is a simple substance with accidents that are divisible into parts such as DNA? This is the route Aquinas would walk. Human beings are fundamentally composed of matter with the form of a human being. Their parts are also human since the form of a human being is inherent in every single part. The substance determines the parts to be what they are. When separated from the form of a human being—for instance, in a test tube—DNA is a different substance because an isolated DNA string is merely molecular, but when present in a human being, DNA is part of a much larger whole—therefore its substance is human. The bottom line is that a human being must be defined first before parts such as DNA can be included in that definition. The substance of human beings causes the parts to be what they are.

DNA's Causa Efficiens

Based on the previous analysis, the *causa materialis* of DNA turns out to be rather inadequate on its own. There is much more needed to make DNA work the way it works. Let us see which other factors come into play. In other words, what is the *causa efficiens* that makes DNA work the way it works?

First of all, DNA can never do anything on its own. It is not even capable, as many still believe, of self-replication—making copies of itself on its own. The idea that DNA replicates itself by using the code provided by the DNA leads to a terribly circular problem. To put this in Thomistic terminology, a *causa materialis* can never be its own *causa efficiens*. As a matter of fact, DNA copies are indeed manufactured out of small molecular bits and pieces but not without the use of elaborate cell machinery that is made up of proteins and other molecules. If DNA is put in the presence of all the pieces that will be assembled into new DNA, but without the presence of assembly machinery, nothing happens. It is actually the surrounding cellular machinery that makes sure that old DNA strands are replicated into new strands. This process is analogous to the production of copies of a document by a photocopier—a process that would never be described as "self-replication." Think of viruses, which are essentially pure DNA or RNA; their DNA or RNA cannot do anything until they penetrate, like a Trojan horse, into the interior of a "living" cell that has the right machinery to offer.

There is a second caveat that not all geneticists seem to be aware of. DNA on its own does not produce anything, not even proteins. The role of DNA is to provide a specification regarding how amino acids are to be strung together into proteins by some synthesizing machinery, but this string of amino acids is not yet a protein. First of all, parts of the string may have to be excised before the string has the correct composition. Second, to become a protein with physiological and structural functions, it must be folded into a three-dimensional configuration that is only partly based on its amino-acid sequence and is also determined by the cellular environment and by special processing proteins. DNA is effectively one-dimensional, but proteins are three-dimensional.

Insulin for diabetics makes a case in point. Recently, the DNA coding sequence for human insulin was inserted into bacteria, which were then grown in large fermenters until a protein with the amino-acid sequence of human insulin could be extracted. But amino-acid sequence alone does not determine the shape of a protein. The first proteins harvested through this process did have the correct sequence, but were physiologically inactive. This is what happened: The bacterial cell had folded the protein incorrectly. Somehow the DNA does not "know" how to fold a protein so as to make it work. This problem may surface more often than initially thought. Amyloids, for instance, are insoluble protein aggregates that arise from inappropriately folded polypeptides naturally present in the body. These wrongly folded structures may even play a role in various neurodegenerative disorders, including Alzheimer's disease.

A similar situation may also explain how prions cause diseases such as Creutzfeldt–Jakob disease. Prions propagate by transmitting a protein in a wrongly folded state. When a prion enters a healthy organism, it induces existing, properly folded proteins to convert into the disease-associated prion form. Somehow the prion acts as a template to guide the folding process of more proteins into prion form. These newly formed prions can then go on to convert more proteins themselves; this triggers a chain reaction that produces large amounts of the prion form. Such a process is only possible because DNA does not quite "know" how to fold proteins.

Then there is a third consideration to mitigate the widely heralded role of DNA. The proteins that DNA produces may not only require a special folding process—they are also still incomplete, as they may need the presence of additional, non-protein factors that are not under direct DNA control but rather come from the environment. Many proteins, especially those with enzymatic activity, need "helper molecules" to perform their biological function. These factors can be loosely bound, so-called coenzymes, or tightly bound, so-called prosthetic groups. The enzymes alcohol dehydrogenase and DNA polymerase, for instance, require the presence of zinc as a cofactor for them to work. The hemoglobin protein in red blood cells, to take another example, requires the presence of a prosthetic heme group that contains iron in its center. The most common cofactors are metal ions such as iron, zinc, and copper; other cofactors are vitamins (e.g., vitamin C) or are made from vitamins (e.g., from B vitamins). Without these cofactors, many DNA products cannot function properly, because DNA only delivers an incomplete product.

It could be argued that the above considerations have effectively taken DNA off its acclaimed pedestal. DNA is in essence merely a *causa materialis*. This would entitle us to make the following daring statement: DNA is not the "secret of life"—as so many seem to think—but it is rather the other way around: life is the "secret of DNA." The *causa materialis* is not enough on its own to make DNA do what it does. Ironically, the American molecular biologist Walter Gilbert had the audacity to claim that "when we have the complete sequence of the human genome we will know what it is to be human." This might well be called professional—or actually unprofessional and unscientific—arrogance. If nothing else, it definitely amounts to poor philosophy.

DNA's Causa Formalis

Geneticists love to claim that DNA contains the genetic information for a living organism. Interestingly enough, the word "information" is derived from the Latin verb *informare*, which means to "give form." This suggests that we are dealing here with a *causa formalis* in the sense given by Aquinas. Many other words popular among geneticists—such as "code," "program," and "blueprint"—are of a similar nature. What are we to make of this?

DNA is not simply a chemical molecule but a biological structure that can be understood and explained in terms of programs and blueprints. In other words, to explain the working of DNA, we look not just to chemistry and physics but also to information technology. The message of a code may be analyzed into its particular constituents, but it cannot be reduced to them. If the same information can be transported by different vehicles—such as pen strokes on paper, currents in computers, DNA in the cell— the conclusion would be that information is not identical to its carrier. Talking of "code" is actually "design" talk, which is foreign to physics. This is a clear indication that we are dealing here with a *causa formalis*—the form behind the in-form-ation. The genetic code as such is immaterial and should be distinguished from the material it is written on. As George Gilder of the Kennedy Institute at Harvard University puts it, "Information is defined by its independence from physical determination: If it is determined, it is predictable and thus by definition not information." Put in Thomistic terms, at the heart of the material we find the immaterial, but the immaterial needs the material, for without a signal there could be no message.

Crucial in information theory is the separation of content from the vehicle that transports it. In a computer, as information theory shows, the content is manifestly independent of its material substrate. There is a "physical layer" of silicon chips and the like at the "bottom," responsible for sending bits of information. This layer is not concerned with the meaning of bits and deals with physical connections only. As George Gilder puts it, "No possible knowledge of the computer's materials can yield any information whatsoever about the actual content of its computations." Whereas physical constraints can be of any kind—e.g., any speed or position or temperature—biological constraints represent a specific selection of constraints from a multitude of physically equivalent alternatives. We could even argue that the laws of genetics are not the result of the structure of DNA, but rather DNA has been "chosen" from among many potential molecular candidates precisely because it fits the requirements of an evolved genetic system.

If the sequence of DNA were fully predetermined by chemical bonds, DNA would not be able to store or convey any information at all. Purely physical processes would be bound to lead to a destabilization of information. A mixture of chemical substances will ultimately act according to the second law of thermodynamics and revert to the most probable state of chemical equilibrium. Instead, DNA bears information, but as with a sheet of paper or a computer memory chip, its chemistry is irrelevant to its content. So it is not the *causa materialis* of DNA itself that creates information. DNA may be a carrier for information, but in itself it is not information. It is a "neutral" carrier of information, independent of its chemistry and physics. Its information is transferred through physical and chemical carriers—but it is not specified by physical and chemical forces. As George Gilder puts it, "The genetic 'words' of the DNA code are no more dictated by the chemistry of their DNA carrier than the words in Scrabble are determined by the chemistry of their wooden racks." Seen from a purely physico-chemical perspective, any order in the DNA sequence is possible. Therefore physics and chemistry cannot specify which order will in fact succeed in functioning as a code.

Apparently, there is an inverse relationship between chemical necessity and biological information. The more necessity dominates, the less information can be encoded in the DNA. To explain this difference, we could use the analogy of the difference between the information that we wish to convey and the material requirements of writing—that is, the ink and paper and formation of the letters. If the ink or the letters dictated the content of the message, we would be severely limited in terms of the information we could communicate. The late physical chemist Michael Polanyi translates this as follows: "[As] the arrangement of the printed page is extraneous to the chemistry of the printed page, so is the base sequence in a DNA molecule extraneous to the chemical forces that work in a DNA molecule."

Although the DNA code may have coding units—so-called codons, composed of three nucleotides—the "meaning" of these codons is not fixed but depends on their surroundings—at the higher level of a *causa formalis*, so to speak. George Gilder calls this "the primacy of the word over the flesh," comparable to regular language in which certain words receive a meaning from their context. The same holds for DNA. The Harvard geneticist Richard Lewontin likes to use the DNA sequence of the nucleotides G-T-A-A-G-T as an example. Usually the cellular machinery will read this as a two-codon instruction to insert the amino acids valine and serine into a growing protein chain. However, sometimes this very same sequence is read as a code that regulates the expression of a neighboring gene, and at other times it acts as a "blank" separating two different DNA sequences. This makes the neuroscientist Jonah Lehrer remark, "Our human DNA is defined by its multiplicity of possible meanings; it is a code that requires context." In order to find out which interactions cause which interpretation of the very same DNA sequence, we need some kind of *causa formalis* approach. Genes may no longer be discrete units in a "material" sense, but they still are in a "formal" sense.

As stated above, any arrangement of the four bases in DNA is compatible with the laws of physics and chemistry. But in terms of biological information, it is just the particular order that makes all the difference. But there is more to it. Not only must the scientist recognize the existence of information, but in some sense the organism must "recognize" it too. That's where Aquinas's concept of a matter–form composite comes in again. DNA is a material entity, whereas information is an immaterial entity. Together, the material and immaterial make for a matter–form composite. The paper that holds a message did not give rise to the message it conveys. The message is in the "form" of the paper, but the paper is just the material carrier of the message.

The concept of "form" indicates that even living things cannot be understood by an analysis of "matter" alone. Matter is ultimately irrelevant to the information it carries. The reference to a code is not on the same explanatory level as the laws of physics and chemistry. In the words of Marjorie Greene, "The explanation through reference to a code is a hierarchical explanation that adds additional constraints on the operation of the system." When the code becomes disorganized, the organism may die, although there is nothing wrong in a physical or chemical sense.

So what is the "form" behind DNA's in-form-ation? Ultimately it is the *form* of the entire organism. When we talk about the DNA of a human being, we are no longer talking about DNA in a test tube, but about DNA in a cell, in an organ, and ultimately in a human body. It is then that the *form* of a human being becomes the "agent" able to structure, regulate, constrain, channel, and empower the DNA—which is from now on *virtually* present as a part of a larger whole (see chapter 3). The whole is more than the sum of its parts, as Aristotle used to say. Aquinas, in the footsteps of Aristotle, believed that it was false to say that being is defined only by the sum of its parts. It is the whole of the organism that is the *causa formalis* behind all of its parts, including its DNA parts. Therefore, we may conclude again that DNA—which is only a part of the whole organism—is not the secret of life; rather, it is the life of the organism—which is the whole in its entirety—that is the secret of DNA.

One word of caution, though, about this "information" terminology. Whereas the information held by text can be instantiated in many different physical forms—written in ink or pencil or chalk, on paper or on slate, in electronic characters on a screen, or not written at all but spoken—the causal properties of DNA, including the effects it has on an organism's development, require it to be in the physical form that it is and no other. A text printout of C's, G's, T's, and A's on paper would not do the job. So the analogies with concepts such as "information" and "code" borrowed from information sciences may be helpful to a certain extent, but also deceiving. As John Haldane remarks, DNA may be similar to a "blueprint" in one respect—in that it guides the development of the organism—but the obvious disparity is that the blueprint does not enter into the structure of the house, whereas the genes that contain the DNA, and whose sequence guides the development of a growing organism, remain within—as parts of the embryo, fetus, infant, adolescent, and so on throughout life.

To say that the information process is guided by DNA can also be deceiving in another way. In the analogy of building a house, we could liken the DNA to specifying the materials to be used, but that still leaves the question open of where the floor plan comes from. It is definitely not the molecular composition of organisms that determines their form. But if the form is not specified by DNA molecules, where then does it come from? Since the same DNA code is present in each part of the body, what then tells it which part to develop and where it ought to deploy? Information does not interpret itself.

As a matter of fact, for more than three decades we have known that the program determining the development of the fertilized egg cell during the early stage of embryonic development is an "epigenetic" program, consisting of mRNAs, proteins, hormones, neurotransmitters, nutrients, etc., arranged in a strictly determined spatial order. The lack of this epigenetic program in regular somatic cells, which have all the genetic material that the fertilized egg cell is in possession of, is the reason why somatic cells fail to develop into an adult organism. To put this in terms of act and potency, genes are potentially phenotypes, and phenotypes are activated genes.

Epigenetics may be on its way to becoming a hot new field of biology. It is the acknowledgment that genetic information is more than a series of genes or DNA strings. Epigenetics is the study of changes in gene activity that are not caused by changes in the DNA sequence. Behavioral epigenetics, for instance, attempts to provide a framework for understanding how the expression of genes is influenced by experiences and the environment to produce individual differences in behavior. Our genome acts more like an "archive," but the question remains of how it is determined *what* to use from this archive *when*, *where*, and *how*. Perhaps we can illustrate the problem we have here in terms of the following simple question: Because there are genes for eye color, color blindness, etc., would the sum of all these genes together be enough for having eyes? Most likely not, because a gene does what the program dictates, not the other way around—the program does not do what a gene dictates. In other words, the program goes beyond the dictates of individual genes and their DNA. It resides at a "higher level."

So Aquinas would be right to speak in all these cases in terms of a *causa formalis*. Coming from a Thomistic tradition, Jacques Maritain would word it this way: a form "orders each part to the whole and gives to the organism its reality as a living being. It is the principle of life, the ordering 'form' of the living body." All sciences, including genetics, presuppose form, even if they thereafter often attempt to ignore it. To take up the example we used earlier in this chapter, human beings are fundamentally composed of matter with the form of a human being. The parts are also human since the form of human beings is inherent in every part of a human being. The substance of human beings causes the parts to be what they are. Any individual atom separate from the form of the body is substantially different, because the substance of the atom is atomic, but an atom in a human body is only part of the whole—and therefore its substance is human. Aquinas would most likely agree that DNA in a test tube is different from DNA in a human body. In a human body it is "virtually" present, but now under the form of a rational animal. Even when the DNA code undergoes changes and mutations, it remains the DNA of a human being.

So we end up with a conclusion that Norbert Wiener from MIT worded as follows: "Information is information, neither energy nor matter." He is right, information is indeed neither matter nor energy, but it does need matter for its embodiment as well as energy for its communication. There is no information without a carrier; without a signal there could be no message. "Information" is in the DNA molecule as an arrangement of parts, but it is in and of itself not composed of physical elements. It comes ultimately from the *form* of the entire organism.

DNA's Causa Finalis

The question we have to address next is what DNA information is "for," what its effect is. If a heart is for pumping and an eye for seeing, what then is DNA for? This question is in search of the *causa finalis*, in Aquinas's terminology.

For a while, geneticists held on to what they literally called their "central dogma," which says, "DNA makes RNA makes protein"—that is, a one-directional causal flow, with one item of code, a gene, ultimately making one item of substance, a protein (proteins include also enzymes). So the DNA of a gene can be for the formation of a sequence of amino acids, and all these proteins together allegedly make a body. Since there are four different nucleotides (A, C, G, and T) and twenty different amino involved in protein synthesis, the coding unit of DNA, a codon, must be three nucleotides long, which makes for 64 possible combinations (4^3) and thus leaves room for "synonyms." The codons GCA, GCC, GCG, and GCU, for example, all specify the same amino acid, alanine. To put it differently, although their *causa materialis* is different, their *causa finalis* is the same.

But not all DNA codes have the same kind of effects. Genes come in at least two main forms, expressive and regulatory (although some perform both functions). The expressive (also called structural) genes are those that create the cell proteins needed for structure and metabolism, as mentioned earlier; these we can regard as the "low-level" genes. But before a gene can be expressed, it may have to be "switched on," and this is a function of the genetic regulatory system, the "higher-level" control process of the cell. It has been found that protein-coding regions of genes can be interrupted by DNA segments that play more of a regulatory role. These regions are called either enhancers or silencers. They are short regions of DNA that can be bound with proteins to enhance or silence transcription levels of genes in a gene cluster. Enhancers produce activator proteins that activate the activity of an expressive genes, whereas silencers produce repressor proteins that repress gene activity. Some regulatory DNA segments are actually very short and produce only short strands of mRNA capable of blocking the mRNA of an expressive gene from creating its own regular protein. The picture is getting more and more complicated.

Although we are learning more and more about the human genome, large parts of it are still poorly understood. In between the genes that we know of, there is much more DNA, so-called intergenic DNA. This DNA holds DNA sequences that do not seem to do anything, and are therefore usually called noncoding DNA. The amount of noncoding DNA varies greatly among species, but in the human genome up to 98 percent is considered noncoding DNA. That is quite a bit of DNA that does not seem to be doing much at all—that is why it is often called "junk DNA" in the popular press. Currently, geneticists speak rather in terms of "noncoding," "neutral," or "silent" DNA. To declare this 98 percent chunk of DNA to be mere "wasteland" is rather premature. Just because the function of a specific region is not known does not mean that it has no function at all. Absence of evidence is not evidence of absence.

Although we may not know what these "silent" DNA sections are for, the question remains whether they are really "for" nothing—or do they rather have a hidden function, some kind of *causa finalis*? It is becoming more and more evident that this "silent" DNA is not as useless as initially thought. This alleged "wasteland" has proved to be a repository for a variety of functions that are part of normal, and even critical, cellular processes.

What then could the function of this "silent" DNA be? There are several possibilities. Some sequences may have no biological function for the organism itself, but they do for some "intruder" such as endogenous retroviruses. When a retrovirus is inserted into oncogenes, it can convert normal cells into cancer cells. This DNA is not functional for the host organism, but it obviously is for the intruder. Then there is at least one more function "silent" DNA may have for the organism itself—redundancy. Noncoding DNA appears to harbor large numbers of tandem, repetitive DNA sequences. These sections are most likely the result of gene duplications, replicated from regular, coding DNA.

How could the creation of gene duplicates ever be advantageous or functional for the organism? Well, the main reason seems to be that this redundancy is a potential source of new useful genes. The duplication of a gene results in an additional copy that is free from selective pressure—that is, mutations of it have no deleterious effects on its host organism (see chapter 9). Thus, copies can accumulate mutations faster than a functional single-copy gene, over the course of generations. This freedom from consequences may allow for the mutation of novel genes that could potentially code for a new function and thus increase the fitness of the organism.

A classic example of this is the human beta-globin cluster. It is composed of five genes located on a short region of chromosome 11. There is actually also a sixth gene, but it is a pseudogene that has a mutation which prevents its expression. The sequences of these six genes are quite similar, which suggests that they originated from duplication of an ancestral beta-globin gene. Together, all five functional genes are responsible for the creation of the beta parts (roughly half) of the oxygen transport protein hemoglobin, but they do so at different moments during development: the epsilon gene is expressed during early embryo development, the two gamma genes during fetal development, the delta gene early after birth, and the beta gene throughout the remainder of the life cycle. These proteins work differently, nicely in tune with certain stages of development.

What is the outcome of all these recent developments in genetics? It seems evident that the *causa materialis* of the genome can no longer be seen as simply "beads on a string." The early molecular gene in biological history did have a beginning and an end, but it turned out to be a stripped gene, that is, a structural gene as part of a wider architectural setting that can vary greatly. Further research has revealed that structural regions can be shared, overlapping, nested, and even physically split; moreover, alternative slicing can produce various products of gene translation, and besides, one product can have multiple functions. Thus, a molecular gene is not a well-defined structure. In a "material" sense, it is not a discrete unit, but in a "formal" sense it is. A molecular gene can be split into several domains (such as enhancer, promoter, suppressor, intron, and exon), but none of these domains is a necessary part of a gene. Yet, the entire genome still remains under the control of DNA's *causa formalis*.

DNA's Causa Exemplaris

How is it possible for DNA to contain the code that regulates the development of any kind of organism? This is not a question about the origin of DNA and its subsequent changes—that is a scientific issue. For Aquinas, this question stands in a much wider context and is ultimately related to God—the Alpha and Omega of all creation. God would be considered the *causa exemplaris* of all of creation. DNA can only contain information because it is a reflection of what is in God's mind. In other words, DNA as a secondary cause can exist only because of the Primary Cause.

Interestingly enough, Francis Collins—the former longtime leader of the Human Genome Project and currently the director of the National Institutes of Health—explicitly speaks about DNA as "the language of God" and about his project as "laying open the pages of this most powerful textbook." DNA is the "language" in which God created life. Our human DNA is like a "text" that finds its *causa exemplaris* in God, the Primary Cause of everything in this universe. The "text" of human DNA has turned out to be three billion letters long, written in a four-letter code. This goes almost beyond our imagination; a live reading of that code, day and night, at a rate of one letter per second, would take thirty-one years.

A problem for this view of a *causa exemplaris* might be that the DNA code is subject to and has been changed by what is called "random" mutations. The word "random" is a scientific, actually a statistical, concept. When people toss a coin, there is randomness involved because the outcome is independent of what the one who tosses the coin would like to happen, and it is also independent of previous and future tosses. Yet, in the aggregate, we are able to make predictions to a certain extent in terms of probabilities. On the other hand, there is no purpose or direction in randomness or chance; if you do not believe this, just test it at a slot machine. In short, most biologists consider DNA a random product of evolution, based on random mutations (see chapter 9). That does not sound good for its *causa exemplaris*.

How could such a random product ever be God's language? In other words, how can nature's randomness and God's providence ever go together? Does one not have to go at the cost of the other? Not so for Aquinas. On the one hand, Aquinas does not dismiss or deny chance or randomness in God's creation. According to William E. Carroll, Aquinas "argues that God causes chance and random events to be the chance and random events which they are, just as he causes the free acts of human beings to be free acts." On the other hand, Aquinas does not deny or dismiss providence. He once said, "Whoever believes that everything is a matter of chance, does not believe that God exists." He explains that "the causality of God, who is the first agent, extends to all being. . . . It necessarily follows that all things, inasmuch as they participate in existence, must likewise be subject to divine providence."

How can Aquinas defend both sides at the same time? In his *Summa Theologiae*, his reasoning is that the presence of chance and contingency in nature shows that nature requires a divine Creator in order to exist. And at the same time he says in his *Summa contra Gentiles* that because of the order and hierarchy of causes, "the order of divine providence requires that there be chance and fortune in reality." For example, we cannot know the outcome of a dice roll before it occurs, nor can we explain how it turns out the way it does; there are too many variables and causes acting together, such as the speed at which we throw the dice and the way the dice bounce when they first impact the table. Yet divine providence is a higher cause than all of them combined, and nothing, not even events we perceive as random, escapes it. Truly, God does not play dice, as Albert Einstein famously said—rolling the dice is part of secondary causes, but not of the Primary Cause.

Apparently, Aquinas is talking about two different levels, forcing us to make a clear and important distinction between randomness in science and providence in religion. When we speak of randomness in science, according to the particle physicist Stephen M. Barr, we are talking in statistical terms, in the sense of how things in this universe are related to one another. But when we speak of providence in religion, we are talking about how things in this universe are related to God—not to one another.

Interestingly enough, devotees of randomness in science make chance somehow the ultimate primary cause of this universe, thus making randomness a cause that needs no further explanation. However, if randomness is the basis for change in the universe, it must be a secondary cause and cannot be itself a primary cause. Chance events occur *within* nature, so chance cannot be a primary cause. That's why it makes no sense to capitalize "Chance" and declare it a self-explanatory principle of nature—something like the blind deity of "Doom" or "Fate." Randomness plays a very legitimate role in the sciences, but not so in the whole of the universe. It is God who is the ultimate cause of the randomness that brings about new species. Randomness is just another created entity, another secondary cause—and therefore not the ultimate explanation of everything in this universe.

Therefore, anything that seems to be random from a scientific point of view may very well be included in God's eternal plan. How can that be? Well, Aquinas held that God's position with respect to time is such that, unlike us, He does not have to wait for the future to unfold in order to know its contents. God is in no way a temporal being, but rather the creator of time, with complete and equal access to all of its contents. But if God exists entirely outside of time—in a kind of eternal present to which all that occurs in time is equally accessible—He would indeed be able to comprehend all of history, the past and the present as well as the future, just as though they were now occurring. We may not know what the future holds, but we do know that God holds the future.

As stated above, creation by God accounts for the existence of things, not for changes in things (see chapter 6). An evolving universe is still a created universe. No explanation of change in the cosmos or in evolution, no matter how radically random or contingent we claim this change to be, challenges the metaphysical account of creation, that is, of the dependence of the existence of all things upon God as the Primary Cause of all secondary causes (see chapter 3). The concept of randomness in science is about the relationship between secondary causes, but it has nothing to do with how secondary causes are related to the Primary Cause. How things in the universe are related to the Maker of the universe is a completely different story. That is the reason why something like DNA can be seen as a *causa materialis* in science—a sequence of nucleotides—and at the same time as a *causa exemplaris* in religion—the language of God. DNA may appear to us to be driven by chance, but seen from God's perspective, the outcome would be entirely specified. We just do not have God's point of view.

To open the mind for further study:

Collins, Francis S. *The Language of God*. New York: Free Press, 2006.

Robison, Shea. "Did Aristotle and Aquinas Discover DNA?" https://epigeneticsguy.wordpress.com/2014/08/10/epigenetics-and-environmental-ethics-iv-did-aristotle-and-aquinas-discover-dna/

Simon, Michael A. *The Matter of Life: Philosophical Problems of Biology*. New Haven, CT, and London: Yale University Press, 1971.

Verschuuren, Gerard. *It's All in the Genes! Really?* Charleston, SC: CreateSpace, 2014.

9

Aquinas and Evolutionary Biology

WHEN AQUINAS calls each human being a rational animal (*animal rationale* or *rationabile*), he is not talking evolution. He is merely categorizing human beings as animals, because they share all characteristics that animals have—they all breed, feed, bleed, and excrete. But at the same time, he distinguishes them as unusual and very peculiar animals who have the faculties of reason and intellect (see chapters 4 and 10). Aquinas did not need any kind of sophisticated biology to see the truth that humans are first of all animals. Obviously, Aquinas did not know about evolution and evolutionary biology—the concepts associated with these would arise some six centuries later. That makes it even more intriguing to see how his intricate philosophy with its timeless distinctions would handle such a confrontation.

Had Thomas Aquinas known about evolution, he would probably have said that evolution offers us a scientific account of changes, of how a later state of the material world might have emerged from an earlier state—whereas creation offers us a metaphysical account of where the material world itself ultimately comes from. Creation is about the Primary Cause, whereas evolution would be about secondary causes such as mutation, speciation, and natural selection. Creation creates something out of nothing, whereas evolution produces something out of something else—by following biological laws in the same way as planetary motion follows physical laws. God does not make things Himself, but He makes sure they are being made through His laws. God as the First Cause operates in and through secondary causes, including the causes of evolution. That would probably be Aquinas's take.

Interestingly enough, Charles Darwin explained the natural evolution of species as due to what he called "secondary causes." In distinguishing "secondary causes" from "primary causes," Darwin adopted a metaphysical principle that was originally formulated by Aquinas. This allowed him to say, "To my mind it accords better with what we know of the laws impressed on matter by the Creator, that the production and extinction of the past and present inhabitants of the world should have been due to secondary causes, like those determining the birth and death of the individual." Kudos to Darwin, but first of all to Aquinas!

The Causality of Evolution

So let us analyze evolutionary theory in more detail with the help of Aquinas's philosophy and his powerful distinctions. We will do so by using his fivefold causality again (see chapter 3).

Causa Efficiens *of Evolution*

The two main factors considered in neo-Darwinism as the driving force of evolution are mutation and natural selection. There may be other factors involved, such as migration, sampling, catastrophes, and isolation, but we will limit our discussion to these two.

To begin with, mutations are random and permanent changes in the DNA sequence of a gene, thus producing new alleles (see chapter 8). Mutations are the main source of genetic variability. Let us discuss first what the word "random" may refer to.

By "random" biologists mean several things. First of all, mutations are considered random in the sense of "spontaneous." We know that certain factors increase mutations, but we don't know when they occur. Second, mutations are—as far as we know—"unpredictable" as to where they strike. We cannot predict at what location in the DNA mutations will hit and what changes they might generate there. Third, mutations are random in the sense of "arbitrary," because mutations do not select their target but hit indiscriminately—"good and bad" spots alike, so to speak. Fourth, mutations are also random in the sense of "aimless," because they occur without any connection to immediate or future needs of the organism. There is no physical mechanism that detects which mutations would be beneficial and then causes those mutations to occur, so they lack any "fore-sight."

Randomness in biology is a very technical concept, mainly borrowed from statistics and probability calculus; it is used when events are not correlated with each other. In that sense, mutations are "statistically random"—they just happen one way or the other, but there is no direct connection with other events such as environmental changes or immediate and future needs, so the former do not affect the latter, nor the other way around. But that is also where randomness ends. It certainly does not mean that mutations are random in the sense of being boundless or unrestricted. There are certainly limits to their effects—limits such as energy barriers and surrounding factors. As a consequence, some mutations may be more likely than others—yet they are random in the sense of what we discussed in the previous paragraph.

Most mutations occur at the gene level, by changing the nucleotide sequence of DNA. They usually affect a single nucleotide, but because codons have synonyms, some mutations may have no different effect at all. But if they do, the change may vary from minor to major. When they occur in the promoter region of a gene, they may affect whether the gene comes to expression or not. When they occur in the gene's coding sequence, they may alter the functionality or stability of its protein product. Although we know of harmful mutations, there are also mutations that can be beneficial for the organism in a certain environment. In addition, there are mutations above the gene level, which can create duplicates of a certain section of the DNA code. Apparently, there are many ways new genes and groups of genes can be produced. Studies of the immune system, for instance, have revealed the amazing capacity of genetic systems to rearrange genes in a way that leads to new properties. Then there are many enzymes with quite different functions although they share identical gene pieces. In addition, large segments of DNA can be shifted between chromosomes and even between different species of organisms—so-called transposons.

We discussed already how the creation of gene duplicates may be advantageous for the organism, given the fact that redundancy is a rich potential source of new functional genes (see chapter 8). The duplication of a gene results in an additional copy that is free from selective pressure—that is, mutations of the copy have no direct deleterious effects on its host organism. Thus, it can accumulate mutations faster than a functional single-copy gene, over generations of organisms. This phenomenon is most likely also the explanation of how the human blood-clotting mechanism came along. It follows an intricate cascading route with a dozen or so proteins—also called "factors." Most hemophiliacs carry a mutated version of factor VIII, some of factor IX. Most of these proteins turn out to be related to one another at the level of amino-acid sequence, which is an indication of ancient gene duplications, most likely in "silent" DNA sections. This explanation is even more plausible when we realize that fish have a much shorter cascade of blood-clotting proteins; the longer cascade found in mammals contains some extra proteins very similar to the original ones, which makes it highly probable that these proteins were a result of replicated DNA sections. Our current blood-clotting mechanism is able to stop leaks much more quickly because it evolved from a low-pressure to a high-pressure cardiovascular system—thanks to extra new proteins.

The bottom line is that mutations create variability and diversity in genetic material—such is the part mutations play. But in addition to mutations, evolution works with a second *causa efficiens*, natural selection, which makes a "selection" from this diversity. Natural selection is not creative; it selects, and thus favors or eliminates what is already there. Unlike mutations, which are considered to happen at random, natural selection is highly "selective." Darwin's theory of natural selection basically attempts to explain nature's flora and fauna in terms of efficient causality—that is, without invoking Designer interventions. Natural selection promotes certain characteristics more than other ones, which increases the frequency of those characteristics in future generations.

Let us use a very simple example of how natural selection works. Among insects, resistance to pesticides has been spreading owing to a high selective pressure for certain mutations. DDT-resistant mosquitoes, for instance, make an enzymatic protein that can accommodate a single molecule of DDT and inactivate it by adding oxygen to a chlorinated side group on its molecule. Every so often, some malaria mosquito has a gene mutation capable of inactivating DDT—perhaps as a result of a duplicated and mutated gene in the "silent" DNA section. From then on, the population of mosquitoes has some genetic diversity in this respect. Natural selection will probably not have much impact until the population has to deal with DDT. From that moment on, the ones with the mutant DNA code have a strong selective advantage over those without it, and thus they will transfer their code much more frequently to the next generation than the carriers of the regular code. As a result, the genetic makeup of the population changes owing to the pressure of natural selection. In time, the entire population may become resistant. Also, migration might effect a similar change in nearby populations.

The neo-Darwinian theory of natural selection basically attempts to explain how the living world changes in terms of physical causes and laws of nature. Darwin used to say that evolution follows laws in the same way as planets and comets follow laws in the physical sciences. Natural selection promotes causes with successful effects. This seems to be "a law of nature" in Darwin's eyes. Selective reproduction is the causal explanation of how something like the green color of certain types of caterpillars could become so widespread in the entire population or species. The green color "made it" among these animals, because it is a successful and functional design in the environment they live in. Natural selection "selects" by favoring causes that have successful effects.

One could question, though, whether natural selection is a *causa efficiens* in the strict sense of the word. Even Darwin himself always felt uneasy about his term "natural selection." As a matter of fact, this term leads us almost automatically to the obvious question: "Selection by whom or by what?" The implication of a "selecting agent" is looming large. Darwin certainly tried to avoid this implication by saying he had as much right to use metaphorical language as physicists do. In his own words, "Who objects to an author speaking of the attraction of gravity as ruling the movements of the planets? Everyone knows what is meant and is implied by such metaphorical expressions." Yet, his colleague Alfred Wallace convinced Darwin to replace the term "natural selection" with Spencer's notion of "survival of the fittest" in the fifth edition of his book. This might suggest that we are dealing here with a *causa finalis* ("fit" for what?) rather than a *causa efficiens*.

Causa Materialis *of Evolution*

Although modern scientists tend to narrow the concept of causality to *causa efficiens* exclusively, this might leave out some important aspects of the discussion—and it certainly does, seen from a Thomistic point of view. When speaking about evolution, we cannot evade the question of what the basic entities or units of evolution are—which could be seen as a *causa materialis* issue. DNA may be the *causa materialis* of mutations, but certainly not of natural selection. Natural selection works on individual organisms, not on their genes or DNA, for the simple reason that natural selection only "sees" entire organisms. It cannot "see" genes or DNA because alleles or DNA sections that do not come to expression in the organism cannot be detected—and thus cannot be subjected to selection. Therefore, it is the organism—not DNA—that is the *causa materialis* of natural selection.

What makes the discussion even murkier is the fact that a biologist such as Richard Dawkins speaks of "selfish" genes involved in a constant "survival battle" with other gene versions in serving their own "interest." By doing so, not only does he make genes the units of selection, he also engages in another highly questionable maneuver. He borrows the term selfishness from the domain of morality—or at least from the realm of human behavior—and uses it as a metaphor for the behavior of genes. So far so good, but then he tries to explain morality and human behavior—including altruism—exclusively in terms of these "selfish" genes. He says about writing his book *The Selfish Gene*, "My purpose is to examine the biology of selfishness and altruism." He treats the biological metaphor of selfishness as the real thing and then uses this analogy to explain human behavior of selfishness and altruism.

That clearly amounts to turning things upside down. The biological metaphor of selfishness is only possible because we already have an understanding of human behavior. So "selfishness" is not a good word for genes. As some have said, we should replace it with "the quality of being copied by a Darwinian selection process." The verdict of the anthropologist Donald Symons might be right: "The anthropomorphism of genes . . . obscures the deepest mystery in the life sciences: the origin and nature of mind" (see chapter 10).

Because genes are just parts of a larger whole—the entire organism, that is—it is this larger whole that is exposed to natural selection. Aquinas taught us how elements are present in compounds, stating that they are not present there actually or potentially, but only "virtually" (see chapter 3). So, while there is only one substance that results from the composition of various elements, the new substance has the powers of the elements that came together in its composition. Aquinas thus says that the elements are not actually in the substance, but they are there virtually, i.e., by their power (*virtus*). So the individual organism is more than the sum of its parts, including its genes and DNA. It is as a "whole" that an organism is subject to natural selection.

Indeed, in terms of natural selection and adaptation, the individual organism seems to be the fundamental unit of operation. But when it comes to evolution, not even the individual organism qualifies, but rather the entire population, and more specifically, the species those organisms belong to. The task of evolutionary biology is to explain new species as arising out of earlier ones in the same way that mountains and lakes are explained as having arisen out of earlier geological formations. One could argue that only thinking in terms of species—rather than individuals—allows us to formulate evolutionary theory. It is not individuals that evolve but groups of individuals—more specifically, populations, or even species.

But now the question arises of whether it is possible for a species to be a *causa materialis* in evolution. Does a species really exist as a unity, or is it merely a category of classification? For a long time, following Linnaeus, a species was considered to be a collective name for a group of animals sharing the same characteristics and thus meeting the requirements of being classified in the same category. The species *Canis lupus*, for instance, was once seen as a collective term for all animals that look like wolves. Being a member of a category is defined and determined on the basis of certain criteria. The consequence of this view would be that criteria common to all members have to be found—some kind of common morphology exemplified by the so-called holotype specimen. This approach led to what is called a "typological" species concept.

What is the problem with this concept that views a species as a group of similar-looking organisms? The main question would be how similar should "similar" be, and where should we draw the line. Even if we adopt Ludwig Wittgenstein's concept of "family resemblances"—with members of a family having overlapping similarities, even if they don't have one essential feature in common—this species concept remains rather hazy. Since the members of any population or species differ from one another in various ways, and since there is no feature or set of features that is both necessary and sufficient for membership, there can be no "specimen" that defines membership. Conceived this way, a species could not really make for a *causa materialis* in evolution.

The solution to this problem has been given by a species concept currently standard among biologists, the so-called biological (or reproductive) species concept: a species is a population of organisms that can breed with one another, but not with organisms of other populations. The members of a species, according to the biological species concept, are bound together by internal gene flow; this gene flow is confined by a set of intrinsic isolating mechanisms, which can be geographical barriers or fertility barriers. Hence, according to this concept, a species is an evolutionary unit kept together by gene flow and isolated from other species by intrinsic isolating mechanisms. It is considered a real entity in space and time—a real *causa materialis* of evolution. Its members may share some similarities, but what is more important is the fact that they are isolated from other groups by reproductive barriers. All we need is family ties, not family resemblances. Similarities as such do not count for much, as they are merely a by-product of reproductive isolation; theoretically, the parts of a species may not even have anything in common but reproductive isolation.

Usually speciation—a lineage-splitting event that produces two or more separate species—starts with some form of geographical isolation. Owing to accumulating mutations, geographical barriers may lead in time to biological barriers, according to the current view among neo-Darwinists. Even if the original physical barrier no longer exists, the two new species may stay reproductively isolated owing to their acquired biological fertility barriers. But there is more. Not all geographical isolation is based on physical barriers such as mountains, deserts, or bodies of water. There are also "barriers" of a different nature—such as the mere physical distance between some members of a population. It sometimes happens that a species forms a "horseshoe" ring of neighboring populations that can still interbreed with adjacent populations, but there may be at least two "end" populations in the series that are too far apart and too distantly related to still be able to interbreed. The question, then, arises of whether to classify the whole ring as a single species (in spite of the fact that not all individuals can interbreed) or to consider each population as a separate species (in spite of the fact that there is still interbreeding with nearby populations). This much is clear: if enough of the connecting populations within the ring perish to sever the breeding connection, the remaining members become two distinct species. It should not surprise us, then, that in an evolutionary context, a clear-cut species concept inevitably becomes a bit fluid. If hybrids are still possible, the speciation process has not yet been fully finalized.

Although there may be different degrees of unity within a species, the core idea is that a species can be seen as a real entity in the process of evolution. Conceived this way, a species can be identified in space and time—a discrete entity in the diversity of nature. It is as real as an individual organism is. So the wolves of the species *Canis lupus*, for instance, are not members of an abstract category but parts of a living whole—they can breed with each other but are isolated from other species. Thanks to speciation, it is believed that species are born, reproduce, and die in a way similar to the way in which organisms do. As a matter of fact, before the rise of modern conservationists, most species did not make it in evolution; they either became extinct or evolved into other species. It's estimated that 99.9 percent of all species that have ever lived no longer exist.

Causa Finalis *of Evolution*

According to Charles Darwin, the effect of evolution is adaptation progressing toward perfection. All evolution, he thought, was an adaptive response to changes, however slight, in external conditions. Natural selection carries the evolutionary process to ever-greater perfection, according to Darwin's own words. In the *Origin of Species*, he uses the word "perfect" seventy-seven times, "perfected" nineteen times, and "perfection" twenty-seven times. However, perfection is not taken in its absolute sense—it is rather relative perfection, as good as it needs to be in order to accomplish what it is supposed to accomplish.

Adaptation is usually understood as a process. However, as a practical term, adaptation is often used for the product itself—those features of an organism that result from the adaptation process. As a matter of fact, most aspects of an animal or plant can be correctly called adaptations, although there are always some features whose function is in doubt. It might be wise, though, to use the term adaptation for the evolutionary process, and the term adaptive trait for the bodily part or function that is the result of this process. In addition, adaptation may refer to both the current state of being adapted and to the dynamic evolutionary process that leads to the adaptation. Confusion abounds.

Soon Darwin discovered that structure and function may not always be in agreement. A trait that used to be an adaptive feature—such as the wings of ostriches and penguins that do not fly, or the webbed feet of upland ducks that rarely go near the water—may still be inherited while no longer beneficial. Environments happen to be volatile. Only an "ideal" world of a stable, unchanging environment would allow metazoans to almost perfectly adapt to the environment and establish a quasi-permanent equilibrium with it. However, our planet, far from a static entity, is a dynamic, ever-changing system.

Besides, there are plenty of reasons why certain adaptive features may have been compromised—for instance, genetic and developmental constraints, past history, opposing selection pressures (sexual selection versus predator selection), and many other factors. Constraints like these may keep adaptations from being more perfect than they actually are; they may be optimal— the best we have—but not perfect. In addition, it is highly questionable whether all of evolution can be described in terms of adaptation. To just mention one single question: Is the four-legged structure of vertebrates a better adaptive trait than the six-legged one of insects? It is hard to see how that could be true.

Because of all these considerations, it might be safer to replace the term "adaptation" with the term "fitness"—also called "Darwinian fitness" (to distinguish it from "physical fitness")—as the *causa finalis* of evolution through natural selection. Functions can be measured in terms of fitness—that is, the expected or actual genetic contribution to future generations. Fitness is defined as the ratio between the number of individuals with a certain trait after selection and the number before selection. So there is still a connection between adaptation and fitness; it is likely that adaptive traits do contribute to the fitness of individuals.

However, there is also a danger here that the idea of "survival of the fittest" becomes a tautology—that is, a statement that is true in every possible interpretation. The argument goes like this: "Who survive? The fittest! Who are the fittest? Those who survive!" We do not need to take this attack seriously, though, for it is based on a terminological mix-up. Biological fitness has actually a double meaning: it refers to the role of an organism as the *causa efficiens* of reproduction, but also to the role of an organism as the *causa finalis* of reproduction. This ambiguity also affects the fitness concept: Darwin's concept of fitness—let's call it D-fitness— is potential reproductive success (*causa efficiens*), but there is also the concept of fitness in the sense of actual reproductive success (*causa finalis*), which is the way the statistician Robert Fisher and some population geneticists use it—let's call it F-fitness. Apparently, the slogan "survival of the fittest" is not a tautology if we take fitness as D-fitness, or reproductive capacity. The principle of "survival of the fittest" asserts that those organisms that are potentially successful in reproduction (D-fitness) are more likely to be also actually successful in reproduction (F-fitness).

After what we have seen so far, it may look like mutation and natural selection are the driving forces behind evolutionary change. Unfortunately, the idea of natural selection seems to imply that an organism is at the mercy of external forces. Reacting to external forces, agents, or conditions is indeed a universal property of all material systems. However, unlike inorganic systems that "passively" *react* to external forces and agents, organisms rather *respond* to external influences—that is, they react "adaptively." Organisms tend to counteract, avoid, overcome, or compensate for the harmful effects of the action of external agents. In addition to holding that the environment is the driving force of the evolutionary change in living systems, we should also realize that it is the living system itself and its inherent properties that determine the evolutionary change and its nature and extent—while the environmental factors represent the conditions that may or may not favor the evolutionary change. So the organism is not just a passive entity in the process of adaptation; it is also actively acting to adapt its structure, function, behavior, and life history to the changing environment—which is sometimes captured with the term "epigenetics." Therefore, the cause of evolutionary change can only be partly found in a *causa efficiens* located in the external environment of organisms; the other part has to be found in the *causa finalis*.

Some people think that the Darwinian mechanism eliminates final causes in biology. Stephen M. Barr is perfectly right when he denies this: "Why do species that take up residence in caves gradually lose the ability to see? Because seeing serves no purpose for them, and so mutations that harm the faculty of sight are not selected against. . . . Darwinian explanations can account for very little indeed without bringing intrinsic finality into the explanation." Interestingly enough, to paraphrase Etienne Gilson, the word "purpose" may have disappeared from science, but not from the minds of scientists. They still have many more purposes in mind than they want to acknowledge.

Therefore, it is very common in biology to make "functional" statements like these: camouflage is "for" deceiving, a heart is "for" pumping blood, the eye lens if "for" vision, hemoglobin is "for" oxygen transportation, and so forth. All of these qualify as a *causa finalis*. One word of caution, though, in this discussion: We should take Aquinas's term *causa finalis* in its original sense—being the effect of a *causa efficiens*, and not so much an anticipated goal or intended purpose. Most biologists like to avoid the term teleology altogether in favor of the term teleonomy, because in their eyes the term teleology may carry some historical baggage—with connotations of intention, purpose, and foresight. They introduced this new term to describe the study of goal-directed functions that are not guided by the conscious forethought of man or any supernatural entity. In this sense, adaptation is based on hindsight rather than foresight.

Whereas artificial selection, as done in selective breeding, promotes causes with a *desired* effect—the purpose of the breeder—natural selection promotes causes with a *successful* effect—which is not necessarily the same as an "intended" effect. Hormones, for instance, do in fact reach their target cells, but not because they have a purpose that makes them intentionally go there; it is the receptors on certain target cells that make hormones attach to their "goal." Even water seeks its own level. However, hormones and water molecules do not seek like we seek—in a purposeful manner, that is—but they do have effects that are built into the cosmic design of creation. Whereas purposes may be something in the mind of a human product maker, functions are a feature of the product itself.

Would this mean the end of *causa finalis* in biology? Certainly not. Aquinas would remind us that even in a cause-and-effect world, there is always finality. He would stress that the effect of any efficient cause is a final cause, which makes finality an inherent part of nature.

Causa Formalis *of Evolution*

The previous analysis of modern evolutionary theory would be incomplete without at least discussing Aquinas's fourth cause, the *causa formalis*—the most forgotten cause in evolution. I would say it is definitely active in there, but usually "hidden" in the concept of "design." Although biologists often use words such as "design-like," they usually gloss over this term, because it seems to call for a design-Designer in science. Yet, they consider the animate world "design-like," just like technology engineers consider the world of technology design-like. A heart is "for" pumping as much as a pump is "for" pumping; camouflage is "for" deceiving, just like a knife is "for" cutting. In all such cases, the results must be design-like, because if they were not, they simply would not work in solving the problems they face. If the eye lens, for example, did not function like a physical lens, one would not see very well. That's why a mechanistic approach in science works so well. Birds must follow the same aerodynamic laws as planes—otherwise they surely fall from the sky—and likewise fish must follow the same hydrodynamic laws as submarines do.

The term "design" is actually a teleological concept—whether biologists like it or not, or acknowledge it or not. We should realize, though, that there is some confusion lurking here, because the word "design" in English can refer simply to pattern, or to purpose, or to both. It tends to conflate a formal cause with a final cause. Richard Dawkins, for instance, maintains that Darwinian evolution is not teleological, as the term "selection" in "natural selection" suggests. He considers natural selection to be simply a filter to which a pool of randomly generated mutations is subjected. When he says, "Each generation is a filter, a sieve; good genes tend to fall through the sieve into the next generation; bad genes tend to end up in bodies that die young or without reproducing," he seems to forget that the terms "good" and "bad" already are teleological terms. This filter does not just randomly filter; it filters according to design criteria. That's where teleology comes in. The result may not be an "intended" effect, as in artificial selection, but it is at least more or less a "successful" effect in evolution. Well, here comes a surprise: "success" is in itself a teleological concept that is connected with another teleological concept, "design."

Teleology embodies the idea that nature has "goals" and does things "in order to…" or "for the sake of…" Many biologists think that Darwin banned the "design" concept once and for all from biology. George Bernard Shaw once said that Charles Darwin had thrown William Paley's "watch" into the ocean. Well, what Darwin may have thrown away was Paley's "watchmaker," but certainly not his legendary watch; if he did throw anything away, it was Paley's design-Designer, but certainly not the design concept itself. The concept of "design" is an artifact-based analogy that is as basic to Darwinism as it is to Paley's natural theology. Since the heart has a design like a pump, it is a successful design "for" circulating blood. Apparently, Darwin did not discard design or what comes with it, teleology. As Michael Ruse observed, after Darwin, the heart still existed "for" circulation; the cause of its existence may have been different, but its teleology was not. As a matter of fact, Darwin put purpose, function, and usefulness back into the picture.

This takes us to the heart of the matter: Why do certain biological designs "work," and why are they "successful" and "effective" in reaching their "goal"? What is it that makes them "fit" to certain degrees? Fit for what? Or put differently: What is it that carries them through the filter of natural selection? True, these are not physical but metaphysical questions, located in a "meta-realm" beyond, behind, beneath, outside, or underlying the regular physical realm—but that is not to say those questions do not exist. Yet, as a scientist, Darwin decided to leave such questions untouched. Is that possible? Aquinas would say it's not. Why?

The universe has an overall set of restraints harnessing individual designs and making them "fit" or "successful" to a certain degree. Without a metaphysical design in the "background," biological as well as technological designs could not work at all. A heart could not pump blood if it did not follow hydrodynamic laws; a bird's wing would not let the bird fly if it did not follow aerodynamic laws. It is the "rules and laws of the cosmic design" that restrict the range of possible end results. It is the *cosmic* design that explains which *biological* designs are successful in reproduction and survival—as much as the cosmic design regulates which bridges are successful technological designs. Natural selection can only select those specific biological designs that follow the rules and laws of the cosmic design (again, designers, engineers, and architects must do the same thing).

Leon Kass, a University of Chicago professor and physician, could not have worded it better: organisms "are not teleological because they have survived; on the contrary, they have survived (in part) because they are teleological." To put it differently, organisms have survived because their biological design squares well with the cosmic design. They "fit" in. They must have "something" in their biological design that carried them through the filter of natural selection. This "something" is a fit with the cosmic design. It is the cosmic design that regulates which biological designs "work," and thus are successful. If hemoglobin, for instance, does not have the "right shape," it causes red blood cells to "sickle"—in which case it is a rather unsuccessful biological design, as it violates the laws of the cosmic design.

Each time biologists speak of being "fit" or "successful," they are actually talking teleology—or teleonomy, if you prefer. Certain biological features of organisms are "successful" and "effective" in reaching their "goal" because they have a design that enables such a goal. If they were not design-like, they simply would not work.

Therefore, criteria of fitness are intricately connected with the design concept, which could easily be seen as the *causa formalis* of evolution. Natural selection does not create the fit—it only selects what fits. A good fit comes from somewhere else—the cosmic design. The fittest are not defined by their survival—that would create a tautology—but by their design. Consequently, biological functionality is not an outcome of natural selection but a condition for natural selection. Natural selection does not explain functionality but uses functionality in order to select. Like causality, functionality is one of those universal principles we talked about earlier as being different from scientific generalizations.

In this discussion about the *causa formalis* of evolution, we should mention again the process of speciation that we referred to earlier in the context of *causa materialis*. It is hard to see how a new species could be the mere outcome of natural selection. Whereas Darwinists think almost exclusively in terms of natural selection and adaptation—small adaptations adding up to new structures—it could be argued that future adaptations are instead dictated by existing structures, not the other way around. The latter view is more focused on an underlying structural base dictating the range of modifications that natural selection can work on. Most paleontologists, morphologists, and taxonomists—unlike most other biologists—see the diversity of organisms in evolution through the lens of taxa that differ from each other through their specific construction, build, or configuration—which are concepts of the *causa formalis* type. If their view is correct, species are not the mere result of natural selection, but instead they determine which modifications are possible for natural selection to work on.

In (neo-)Darwinism, organisms are considered "adaptation machines," and as such sufficient to generate evolution. But the question remains whether all forms in the natural world are exclusively a result of natural selection and adaptation. As a matter of fact, not all biological forms seem to be clear cases of adaptation. Evolution has indeed produced endless variation, but based on a rather limited set of basic designs. Let us ask the question again: Why do vertebrates have a four-legged structure? Is that feature more adaptive than the six legs of insects? Once present, a four-legged structure could indeed evolve in specialized, adaptive ways for running, digging, jumping, etc. But how did that structure itself come along? In terms of mere adaptation, whales would be fish, but they have a very different underlying structure. To prevent this implication, there must be some structural, or organizational, reference implied along with the adaptive one. That's why the *causa formalis* cannot be left out.

Concepts such as build, form, or organization—which are of the *causa formalis* type—seem to be indispensable in this discussion. New forms of life embody new operational principles. So it might be useful to distinguish different "thresholds" as an indication for the resistance against changes in evolution. The species border displays a comparatively low threshold, low enough to permit further adaptation to the environment, and high enough to assure reproduction. On the other hand, there may be higher thresholds that coincide more or less with the borders created by taxonomists around an order, a class, or a phylum. These thresholds make for structural restraints in evolution.

Causa Exemplaris *of Evolution*

The previous discussion about a "cosmic design" inevitably leads us to the following question: Where does this cosmic design come from? For Aquinas, the answer can be found in the *causa exemplaris*. In his philosophy, it is the mind of God that is the source and origin of this cosmic design. Therefore, the cosmic design is an intelligent design, and this makes the universe intelligible and comprehensible. Somehow Paley's watchmaker is back again. Our universe was created with an underlying cosmic design that regulates what is and what is not possible in this world. All our laws of nature are part of this cosmic design. The chemical element carbon (C), for instance, has the "built-in" or "spontaneous" capability to form very long chains of interconnecting C–C bonds, and this allows carbon to form an almost infinite number of more or less successful organic compounds. This is the reason why our entire organic chemistry is carbon based; indeed, carbon is the "favorite" building block of the living world on Planet Earth. So it should not surprise us that carbon is an essential part of DNA as well—that is the way our world was designed. When a die repeatedly lands on a six, we say it must be loaded. Well, our world seems to be "loaded" too—loaded with cosmic design.

When scientists or engineers violate the laws of the cosmic design, they get into real and actual trouble. A bridge that has been designed according to the right laws can stand firm, whereas another bridge collapses because its engineers erred in their calculations—perhaps they had the wrong laws in mind, or at least the wrong thoughts and calculations. If those laws and thoughts were merely creations of the human mind, the construction of a bridge would never depend on the right laws and the right thoughts. It would not make sense to say that competent engineers have better mental habits than their inept colleagues—as David Hume suggested (see chapter 4). There must be more to it.

Something similar can be said about the cosmic design that was implemented in our universe by its Creator. It is hard to see how else the rationality found in science could coincide so closely with the rationality found in the universe; somehow the rationality present in our minds matches the rationality we find in the world.

The mind of God behind the creation of the universe and the evolution of humanity is the best explanation for this mysterious conformity between the rationality of our minds and the rationality found around us. The fact that the universe has an elegant, intelligible, and discoverable underlying mathematical structure calls for an explanation, or otherwise must be left unexplained. The beauty and elegance of the laws of nature and the mathematical equations behind them point to divine design. The philosopher Robin Collins worded it this way: "The beauty, elegance, and ingenuity of mathematical equations make sense if the universe was purposefully designed like an artwork, but appear surprising and inexplicable under the nondesign hypothesis." He refers to Steven Weinberg, a convinced atheist, who admits that "sometimes nature seems more beautiful than strictly necessary." Put differently, God's mind is the *causa exemplaris* of this world.

Intelligent Design?

When we called mutations and natural selection the *causa efficiens* of evolution, we stayed away from the question of whether those two causes really and fully explain the mechanism of evolution. How efficient and sufficient have they been in explaining the course of evolution? In fact, Darwinism and its current version, neo-Darwinism, have been under constant attack for being unfinished and incomplete. As far as this is an internal discussion of biologists, it might just suffice to state that natural selection may not be the end of the story, let alone the only factor involved in evolution. Let us stay out of that discussion here. But there is also another battle taking place, raging mainly outside the scientific community. It is the debate surrounding the so-called *Intelligent Design Theory*, often abbreviated as ID theory.

What are we to make of this discussion when seen from Aquinas's perspective? We need to discuss first what ID theory entails. ID theorists question whether natural causes such as random mutation and natural selection can explain all those stunning cases of "complexity" found in nature. They think that the Darwinian theory of evolution fails to account for life's subsequent complexity, which they call "irreducible." More specifically, these ID advocates have focused their attention on complexities as seen in cell biology—in particular the intricacies of the molecular machinery that resides inside the cell.

One of the classical and dear examples of ID supporters is the bacterial flagellum, which is an "outboard motor" that propels bacterial cells in various directions. Indeed, this flagellum does show quite an impressive case of complexity. The DNA expert Francis Collins—although not a friend of ID theory—describes it this way: "The structure of the flagellum, which consists of about thirty different proteins, is really quite elegant. It includes miniature versions of a base anchor, a drive shaft, and a universal joint. All of this drives a filament propeller. The whole arrangement is a nanotechnology engineering marvel. If any one of these thirty proteins is inactivated by genetic mutation, the whole apparatus will fail to work properly."

ID theorists question whether machinery with this kind of complexity could ever have arisen step by step on the basis of random mutation and natural selection alone. So they maintain that such complexity can only be produced by a Designer's intervention—an intelligent, supernatural cause—in addition to, or even instead of, the natural processes of mutation and natural selection. Their main argument goes along these lines: How could any of these components have evolved "by chance" unless the other twenty-nine had developed at the same time? It does seem rather evident, they argue, that none of these parts could have evolved on a step-by-step basis until the entire structure had been assembled. Just think of all the other examples of complexity that may defy claims made by evolutionary theory—cases such as the human blood-clotting cascade, with its dozen or more interacting proteins, or the complexity of the human eye. Natural selection won't work, so the argument goes, until the entire structure has been assembled at once. Thus, ID theory assumes supernatural Designer interventions.

ID theory has been attacked on two fronts—biology and philosophy. On the biology front, Darwinists have argued that so-called "irreducible" complexity can actually be reduced to step-by-step evolutionary processes of mutations and natural selection—without the need for an additional Designer step. Let us go back to the bacterial flagellum, the poster child of ID fans. Comparison of protein sequences from various bacteria has revealed that several components of the flagellum are related to an entirely different apparatus used by some bacteria to inject toxins into other bacteria. Most likely, the elements of this structure were duplicated in the "silent" parts of DNA and then recruited for a new use, subject to natural selection again. And in turn, this process could go on for other elements. Selection just keeps working step by step—mutation by mutation, gene by gene, organism by organism—until the entire structure has been assembled.

Darwinists claim a similar scenario of a step-by-step selection process for the intricate cascading route of human blood clotting, which involves lots of proteins. Most of these proteins turn out to be related to one another at the level of amino-acid sequence, which most likely reflects ancient gene duplications. Since new copies were not essential for the original function, these copies could gradually evolve to take on a new function—a process driven by the force of mutation and natural selection. So the ID assumption that the entire cascade had to emerge fully functional from the very outset as a complete set of DNA sequences seems to be superfluous.

Some Darwinists use the following analogy to make their case: Once the keystone is placed in an arched stone bridge, the scaffolding can be removed; from then on, removal of any part may cause the bridge to collapse, but that doesn't mean the bridge wasn't the product of a gradual construction process. So when ID theorists raised the objection, "What good is half an eye," Darwinists replied, "Better than no eye at all." This process of gradual construction can be exemplified by the partial clotting cascades found in fish: some of these proteins have a long history in the animal world, starting with a simple cascade—far better than none. But when it had to evolve from a low-pressure to a high-pressure cardiovascular system, our blood-clotting mechanism had to gain the ability to stop leaks much more quickly—which required more proteins. So this mechanism did not come along all at once, but rather step-by-step.

Darwinists could add at least one more argument in this context. Even if there are still cases left of so-called "irreducible complexity," which evolutionary theory cannot explain at this moment, those unexplained cases in no way constitute a victory for ID theory. If one theory loses because it cannot explain certain parts of evolution (yet), that doesn't imply that the competing theory has won the argument. One cannot claim that the unexplained is necessarily unexplainable, the unknown unknowable, the unsolved unsolvable; only time will tell. Such a claim would be similar to the claim of certain physicists that they have not found a certain cause yet, so they erroneously jump to the conclusion that there is no cause at all.

Another strategy of Darwinists is attacking the "intelligent" part of the ID theory. It is easy to bring in many examples of optimal designs—the best of what's available—that are not perfect designs, let alone intelligent designs. The fact that the oxygen carrying protein in human blood, hemoglobin, has an affinity for carbon monoxide that is three hundred times stronger than its affinity for oxygen can be detrimental with even low concentrations of carbon monoxide. That does not seem to be an intelligent design; yet it is optimal, since during the evolutionary process natural selection did not have to deal much with carbon monoxide. Or take the case that during the course of their evolution, ruminants acquired very complicated stomachs (basically a set of four) and a very involved digestive routine. In this case, complexity doesn't seem a plus. Their "inner" life would have been so much simpler had they been given the right digestive enzymes from the outset. Or take the DNA sequence for an enzyme that makes ascorbic acid (vitamin C) in most animals. Many primates, including humans, have a defect in this DNA code. Consequently, these organisms must acquire vitamin C through food rich in vitamin C (which was abundant for arboreal primates anyway), but they did hold onto the original defective DNA code in the "silent" section of their DNA. Why would a Designer first establish the vitamin C pathway, and then abandon it?

Some ID theorists respond that these "imperfections" are not really "flaws" but the deliberate product of the intervention of an Intelligent Designer. By doing so, they make their ID theory an unbeatable theory that explains nothing by explaining everything, which makes for a very unscientific strategy. They love to impress us with examples of complex designs, while turning a blind eye to cases of rudimentary, stunted, or even broken designs. In contrast, neo-Darwinists plainly acknowledge such cases of rudimentary design as "scars" from common descent with modification; they are "leftovers" of originally functional designs that were inherited from ancestors but lost their functionality under different circumstances. The fossils of extinct species are not a record of the Designer's failures.

So far, the arguments against ID theory have come from the biological front. But what about the philosophical front? How would Aquinas assess ID theory? He would probably make the objection that ID theory turns the universe from a comprehensive whole into a defective whole that is not causally complete in itself but requires instantaneous and constant interventions to fill the voids God supposedly left behind in His creation. Curiously enough, ID fans do not apply their design theory to all of the universe but typically limit design interventions to cases in which complexity reaches a threshold of "irreducibility." So, if that threshold of irreducible complexity is not reached, no design inference is warranted. This would mean, according to the philosopher Francis J. Beckwith, "that God creates everything *ex nihilo* and then returns now and again to tidy things up a bit when they seem to be going awry."

In this way, ID theory ignores the distinction Aquinas makes between primary cause and secondary causes, and thus degrades the primary cause to a secondary cause. Aquinas writes, "The same effect is not attributed to a natural cause and to divine power in such a way that it is partly done by God, and partly by the natural agent; rather, it is wholly done by both, according to a different way." Aquinas would stress that God created *ex nihilo* a universe teeming with ends or purposes that depend on laws and principles that cry out for explanation.

ID fans, in contrast, make the primary cause periodically act like a secondary cause working inside the universe. In doing so, they change God into a god of the gaps—a god who fills in the gaps left behind in his allegedly defective design of the universe. This kind of god often proves to be a fleeting illusion, for when the frontiers of science are being pushed back—and they usually are—this kind of god would be pushed back with them as well. The great Scholastic theologian Francisco Suárez put it this way: "God does not intervene directly in the natural order where secondary causes suffice to produce the intended effect." All "things" in the universe—not only those with "irreducible complexity"—have their own natures that direct them to certain ends. And God, who brought the universe into being *ex nihilo*, sustains them all. This makes Francis J. Beckwith claim that Aquinas, though a believer in design, was no advocate of ID theory. ID theory may be not only bad biology but also bad philosophy and bad theology.

Science, including evolutionary biology, deals only with secondary causes. Gaps in the explanatory chain of secondary causes cannot be filled by the primary cause, or by so-called divine interventions, but rather they have to await further scientific developments. If we recognize that there are sciences of nature, then such gaps can only be epistemological difficulties to be overcome. In Thomistic terms, there is no competition between the carpenter and his tools regarding who will take credit for the house being built. So ID fans have basically given up on science ahead of time. They have a "dream," but it turns out to be an "impossible dream." Scientists, on the other hand, expect that all natural phenomena are explainable, since it is their basic belief that nature displays order and intelligibility and is therefore accessible to the human intellect for further investigation. True, any kind of science that oversteps its limits is arrogant, but science that does not go to its limits should be considered a failure. The evolution of the eye caused Charles Darwin much anxiety, yet we have much reason to think that scientific questions will ultimately have scientific answers, without the need for any additional interventions by the Creator. Stanley Jaki hailed this as a metaphysical vision—the idea that "the material realm is fully coherent, that is, it needs no special interventions from an outside factor, such as God, to keep it running."

If there is "intelligence" in creation—and there is no reason to deny this—then it resides in the realm of cosmic design, but not directly or necessarily in the realm of biological designs. Biological designs presuppose an overarching, comprehensive, grand design of the universe, because natural selection must *assume* design but can neither explain nor create it. The cosmic design is indeed an intelligent design, but not in the way ID theory understands it. The cosmic design is an intelligent design inherent in all of creation, rooted in autonomous secondary causes and laws of nature, which steer everything—complex and not so complex—toward an end, thus making the universe intelligible and comprehensible.

This view is in line with the way Aquinas sees intelligence in creation: "We see that things which lack intelligence, such as natural bodies, act for an end, and this is evident from their acting always, or nearly always, in the same way, so as to obtain the best result. Hence it is plain that not fortuitously, but designedly, do they achieve their end." According to Aquinas, everything in the universe, including secondary causes and laws of nature, have their own powers and natures that direct them to certain ends. It is only because of these powers and natures that natural selection can do its work.

So design is not only to be found in "irreducibly complex" biological phenomena—as ID theory claims—but actually in *all* of creation. In Aquinas's view, final causes are built-in and intrinsic to everything in the universe. Natural selection favors those features that have successful effects, goals, or ends. That's how more complex eyes came along—"in order to" see better and better. When there is no more *purpose* for complex eyes, they will gradually deteriorate. The ID search for specific instances of design, on the other hand, tends to obliterate the reasonable Thomistic view that *all* of creation is permeated with design.

Michael Augros makes a strong case for a designed universe. His reasoning is, "If the first cause is intelligent, then all things are the products of its intelligence, and living things are just what they always appeared to be—*designed.*" Then he goes on to say, "Long before they came into being, eyes were meant for seeing; ears were meant for hearing. And the world was meant to produce living beings with eyes and ears. And the world was meant to be seen and heard." He also explains why there can be cases of "bad design." In his own words, "If secondary causes, unlike the Primary Cause, are not infallible, if they are defectible, then we might well blame them, rather than the first cause, for any flaws we find (or think we find)."

Apparently, the human mind has the capacity and power to detect and know that the universe and/or parts of it are designed and thus are the product of mind rather than non-mind. Seen in this light, biological designs are evolutionary products successful to different degrees depending on how well they fit in the cosmic design—with some designs being better than others, or appearing more intelligently designed than others, if you will. If biological designs seem "intelligently designed," they do so in a derivative sense, based on the fact that the cosmic design is the creation of an intelligent mind, which makes the universe intelligible in terms of a fourfold causality—which includes the *causa finalis*.

The Path of Evolution

Had Aquinas known about evolution, he would probably have pointed out the following important presupposition of evolution and evolutionary theory: evolution presupposes the creation of beings that evolve and develop according to the internal laws given to each of them, so that they would develop and reach their full potential. This statement was actually used by Pope Francis in his address to the Academy of Science in 2014. It puts what we have said so far in a wider philosophical framework. It combines the act/potency distinction with the matter/form distinction.

According to Aquinas, matter acquires form and flows toward God in all the diversity of creation as different life-forms emerge. Like cosmic evolution, biological evolution can be considered as the deployment of the potentialities that God has placed within created beings—so that protons act like protons, and eagles act like eagles. Finality in these cases is not something extrinsic to things, but inherent in things themselves. Things act according to their very natures and thus produce specific effects. Their finality does not come from without, but wells up from within.

In terms of forms and formal causes, we could say that the simple forms have an inherent tendency, or *potential*, to give rise to more complex forms that, while composed of these simpler forms, somehow transcend them. A spider is not just the arrangement of various parts. It is alive; it is a living form that transcends its chemical components. All living beings are made of the same material constituents—carbon, hydrogen, oxygen, and so on—but they differ in their organic structures, their forms, which enable them to live different lives. Starting from "prime matter," the universe could go a long way—up to life and even human life—as long as we realize that this prime matter is not a substance and does not exist apart from any particular substance. It is always the matter of some substance that exists. Jacques Maritain—who was raised as a Protestant, became an agnostic before converting to Catholicism in 1906, and helped revive Aquinas for modern times—believed that Aquinas would not have been disconcerted by the concept of evolution, for he would only have had to add the dimension of time to this ascending journey of the forms in order to arrive at a philosophical understanding of it.

Earlier in this chapter, the concept of "cosmic design" was introduced as shorthand for the built-in finality and potency of the created world. Perhaps we could add another component to this concept—the so-called *anthropic principle*. There are many versions of this principle, but it typically asserts that our universe is uniquely "fine-tuned" to give rise to life, and even human life. The conditions that enable life in the universe can only occur when certain universal fundamental physical constants lie within a very narrow range. Therefore, if any of several fundamental constants were only slightly different, the universe would most likely not be favorable for the establishment and development of matter, astronomical structures, elemental diversity, or life as we understand it. In other words, the odds against a universe like ours appear to be enormous.

What are these fundamental physical constants? They are physical constants that are dimensionless, which means that their values cannot be calculated but rather are determined only by physical measurement. This is one of the unsolved problems of physics, because their numerical values are not understood in terms of any widely accepted theory. As Stephen Hawking has noted, "The laws of science, as we know them at present, contain many fundamental numbers, like the size of the electric charge of the electron and the ratio of the masses of the proton and the electron. . . . The remarkable fact is that the values of these numbers seem to have been very finely adjusted to make possible the development of life." This fact made even the astronomer Fred Hoyle, once an outspoken atheist, exclaim, "A common sense interpretation of the facts suggests that a superintellect has monkeyed with physics, as well as with chemistry and biology."

Examples of these constants are the masses of fifteen fundamental particles, i.e., six quarks, six leptons, the Higgs boson, the W-boson, and the Z-boson. Another constant, required for cosmology, is the cosmological constant of Einstein's equations for general relativity, having a value of approximately 10^{-122}. It is a constant in Einstein's equation of general relativity that when positive acts as a repulsive force, causing space to expand, and when negative acts as an attractive force, causing space to contract. If it were too large, space would expand so rapidly that galaxies and stars could not form, and if too small, the universe would collapse before life could evolve. And then there is the electromagnetic fine-structure constant $\alpha_e \approx 1/137.036$—a pure number without dimension that underpins all the structural activity of biology, physics, and chemistry. A long-sought goal of theoretical physics is to find first principles from which all of the fundamental dimensionless constants can be calculated and compared to the measured values, but so far, this goal has remained elusive. The values of these constants seem to be a given in the cosmic design of this universe.

Not surprisingly, some scientists have come up with a "scientific" explanation for the "oddity" of the universe we live in. One of them is Stephen Hawking. He postulates some "basic stuff" underlying universe formation. His explanation is worded by Michael Augros as follows: "This fertile nothing spews out universes quite randomly, and so the fundamental constants in them must represent nearly all possible quantitative variations. Most of them, presumably, do not allow life. But some of them inevitably will. And the fact that we happen to live in a life-friendly one is neither a matter of design nor a wild coincidence."

Needless to say, in order to get rid of *design*, Hawking had to come up with some wild theory, invented on the spot, without any empirical basis. In that sense, his supposedly scientific theory is worth as much, if not less, than a metaphysical theory of design based on universal principles. No wonder Isaac Newton stated long ago that "God in the beginning formed matter in solid, massy, hard, impenetrable, movable particles, of such sizes and figures, and with such other properties, and in such proportion to space, as most conduced to the end for which he formed them." Indeed, cosmological fine-tuning (CFT) does not imply any intervention by God *during* the evolution of the cosmos; the laws and constants at issue are preordained, built into the very fabric of reality. They are part of the cosmic design.

The following analogy may help explain the importance of the "cosmic design" concept for evolution a bit further. A river follows a "path of least resistance" according to the "topographic design" of the landscape. In a similar way, the "stream" of evolution follows a path somehow regulated by the cosmic design of our universe. In other words, evolution follows the "path of least resistance" in the landscape of the cosmic design. It does not just flow in a random way. Somehow the cosmic design creates the "bed" in which the stream of evolution meanders. The success of any biological design can be explained only against a background of cosmic design.

This is not mere philosophical speculation. Confirming biological evidence can be found, for instance, in the fact that marsupials in Australia and tenrecs in Madagascar have evolved into groups that resemble mammals on the mainland as diverse as hedgehogs, shrews, opossums, mice, porcupines, and even otters—although they are not closely related to any of these groups. This indicates that these two groups must have gone through their own more or less parallel evolution. Although there was some randomness involved during their evolution, both groups evolved in a very similar way.

The "cosmic design" concept also explains how there can be so much potentiality in this universe. The Belgian biochemist, cell biologist, and Nobel laureate Christian de Duve describes the origin of life this way: "The pathway followed by the biogenic process up to the ancestral cell was almost entirely preordained by the intrinsic properties of the materials involved, given a certain kind of environment or succession of environmental conditions." Evolution seems to have a time arrow moving from "less complex" to "more complex."

The emphasis we have placed in the previous paragraphs on secondary causes and their autonomy in steering the course of evolution might easily give us the impression that God has effectively been shut out from this "closed" world of "law and order." That would indeed be the view of *deism*, stating that the world was made by God but as by a watchmaker who makes a watch, lets it run its own course, and then abandons it to itself—the "hands-off" approach, so to speak, of an absent landlord. In contrast to deism, *theism* tells us that the Creator of this world remains very involved with this world, not only by sustaining and preserving what He has created but also by guiding its further development. How would that be possible in a world "bound by law and order"?

To clarify the possibility of God being involved with the course of evolution—not merely as the Creator of laws and secondary causes—we could perhaps use the following analogy. When watching a game at the golf course or the pool table, we see balls following precisely determined courses of cause and effect; they follow physical laws and are subject to rigid rules. Yet there is one element that does not seem to fit in this predetermined picture, in this cascade of causes and effects—the players of the game themselves. Although we have a cascade of physical causes and effects in all these games, there is much more going on in each process—these players have very specific intentions in mind, intentions which elude and transcend the laws of science. They don't go *against* the laws of nature, but they do go *beyond* those laws. People who are unable to look beyond these physical laws and causes are completely missing out on what the game is all about. The players somehow fall outside the realm of the model of physics; they themselves can steer the course of the laws of nature from "outside the model." Something similar could be said about God's work in the process of evolution: He does not go against the laws of nature and its secondary causes—by supplementing or replacing or violating them, as in ID theory—but rather lets them be, while steering them in a certain direction without overstepping the autonomy of secondary causes.

We could conclude and summarize this chapter as follows. There can be creation without evolution, but not evolution without creation, as there must be actual creatures before they can evolve. The way human creatures evolved can be studied by science in terms of secondary causes, but also from a wider perspective with regard to the Primary Cause, who has great plans for His creation. William E. Carroll said it right: "Rather than excluding Darwin from the curriculum, the schools should add Aquinas."

To open the mind for further study:

Barrow, John D., and Tipler, Frank J. *The Anthropic Cosmological Principle*. Oxford University Press, 1988.

Carroll, William E. "Creation, Evolution, and Thomas Aquinas." *Revue des Questions Scientifiques* 171 (4) 2000: 319–347.

Verschuuren, Gerard M. *Darwin's Philosophical Legacy: The Good and the Not-So-Good*. Lanham, MD: Lexington Books, 2012.

10

Aquinas and Neuroscience

THE FINDINGS by contemporary neuroscientists that specific regions in the brain are associated with particular cognitive and emotional functions provide compelling evidence for the idea that the human *mind* has something to do with these *brain* capacities and their localizations. Scanning techniques such as an electroencephalogram (EEG) or functional magnetic resonance imaging (fMRI)—an MRI procedure that measures brain activity by detecting associated changes in blood flow—have opened up the brain for us as the center of various mental activities.

In exploring the complexity of the nervous system, neuroscientists have developed various specializations in the field of neuroscience. They investigate how genes and molecules regulate nerve cell function (cellular/molecular neuroscience), explore how neural systems produce integrated behaviors (behavioral neuroscience), seek to understand how neural substrates create mental processes and thought (cognitive neuroscience), and study the impact of social factors (social neuroscience).

It should not surprise us that impressive discoveries in the field of neuroscience have set the stage for extravagant claims. In the words of the DNA co-discoverer Francis Crick, "You're nothing but a pack of neurons." Back in 1994, he wrote, "The astonishing hypothesis is that you, your joys and your sorrows, your memories and your ambitions, your sense of personal identity and free will are, in fact, no more than the behavior of a vast assembly of nerve cells and their associated molecules." Marvin Minsky, a pioneer in the field of artificial intelligence, added to this that human beings are mere meat-machines—just machines, although made of meat. And the biologist Richard Dawkins likes to declare that

179

mind is only a feature of matter that emerges when matter is organized in certain complex ways.

The general conviction behind such claims is that mental phenomena are identical to neural phenomena, that the mental is "nothing but" the neural, that the mental is just an illusion—in short, that thoughts are merely brain waves. Can these claims withstand further scrutiny?

The Mental Is Not the Neural

There are several reasons why mental phenomena may be not the same as neural phenomena. Some of these reasons are scientific, some empirical, some epistemological, and some just common sense. Let us study them in more detail.

One of the early neurosurgeons, Wilder Penfield, made a compelling case about the difference between mental events and neural events when he asked one of his patients during surgery to try to resist the movement of the patient's left arm, which he was about to make move by stimulating the motor cortex in the right hemisphere of the brain. Then the patient grabbed his left arm with his right hand, attempting to restrict the movement that was about to be induced by a surgical stimulation of the right brain. As Penfield described this, "Behind the brain action of one hemisphere was the patient's mind. Behind the action of the other hemisphere was the electrode." It must be concluded, as the neurologist Viktor Frankl put it, that while the brain conditions the mind, it does not give rise to it. The neurophysiologist Sir John Eccles concluded from experiments like this one "that voluntary movements can be freely initiated independently of any determining influences within the neuronal machinery of the brain itself." In other words, one action had a physical cause, whereas the other action had a mental cause.

Then there is another argument questioning the idea that the mental and the neural are identical. When neuroscientists claim that certain mental phenomena are associated with certain neural phenomena, they cannot conclude that these mental phenomena were *caused* by neural phenomena—correlation doesn't automatically equal causation. The fact that regions light up on an fMRI does not explain whether this lit-up state indicates that such states are causing a certain mental state or just reflecting it. Therefore, we need to find out whether certain mental phenomena are always correlated with certain neural phenomena, and furthermore, whether they are proportional to the intensity of the mental phenomena. If such is not the case—and mounting evidence indicates it is not—then the assertion that the mental can be reduced to the neural has actually been falsified. Whereas something like pain, for instance, can be induced in a physical way, there is arguably no evidence that experimental stimulation of specific neuronal areas could produce a specific mental state, let alone a specific thought.

This takes us to a third reason why the mental may not be identical to the neural. Identity is not just a matter of correlation. A certain mental state may be associated with a certain neural state, but that does not entail identity. The mere fact that two entities are correlated means that they must be distinct entities. It is true that my mind can be fully occupied with a specific problem, but it is either false or makes no sense to say that my brain is then fully occupied with that problem. If this is true, then my mind and my brain cannot be identical. The most we could say is that a certain part of the brain is thinking about a certain problem under consideration. Even if every mental event is a brain event, not every brain event is a mental event. If there are mental states that are not brain states, then there must be some properties that distinguish these brain states that are mental states from the brain states that are not mental states. These properties will have to be specifically mental, as no physical property could do the trick.

This takes us to a fourth reason why the mental may be—or some say must be—different from the neural. The German philosopher Gottfried Leibniz once suggested to picture the brain so much enlarged that one could walk in it as if in a mill. Inside, we would observe only movements of various parts, but never anything like a thought. For this reason, he concluded that thoughts must be different from physical and material movements and parts. Nowadays, the mechanical model of cogs and wheels that Leibniz used has been replaced by the chemical model of biochemical pathways, but the outcome is the same. Whereas the brain as a material entity has characteristics such as length, width, height, and weight, the mind does not have any of those; thoughts are true or false, right or wrong, but never tall or short, heavy or light. There are devices for recording neural events, but there are no such devices for mental events. If the mind were merely a brain issue, we would have no way of distinguishing between true and false, or between right and wrong. If the mental were the same as the neural, then thoughts could never be right or wrong and true or false. As John C. Polkinghorne puts it, "Neural events simply happen, and that is that." We can think about sizes and colors of things, but the thoughts themselves do not have sizes and colors.

Once we acknowledge this fourth argument, there is a fifth reason to combat denial of the human mind: it is self-destructive. If the mind were just the brain, its thoughts would be as fragile as the molecules they supposedly came from. It would be sitting on a "swamp of molecules," unable to pull itself up by its bootstraps. Sociobiologists, for instance, claim that we believe what we believe because what we call "truth" emerges from brains shaped by natural selection. But claims like these work like a boomerang. In a similar way, we cannot just deny the mental, because denying the existence of mental activities is in itself a mental activity, and thus would lead to contradiction. Ironically, one cannot deny the mental without somewhat affirming it. Some people, such as the nearly legendary biologist J. B. S. Haldane and the philosopher C. S. Lewis, have worded this paradox along the following lines: if I believe that my beliefs are the mere product of neurons, then I have no reason to believe my belief is true—therefore, I have no reason to believe that my beliefs are the mere product of neurons.

The fact that there is science makes for a sixth argument against the denial of the existence of human mind. In order to make any mental claims, especially in science, such claims need to be validated as being true, otherwise they are worth nothing. If Watson and Crick, or Planck and Einstein, or Darwin and Dawkins, or any other scientists, were nothing but their neurons, then their scientific theories must be as fragile as their neurons.

That would be detrimental to their claims. If our mental activities are only the by-product of neural events, they would be nothing more than illusions, or mere sensations at best. If we were nothing but a "pack of neurons," this very statement that we are making here would not be worth more than its molecular origin, and neither would we ourselves who are making such a statement be worth more than our molecular origin. So all the theories scientists have come up with must be more than neural activities, otherwise they would sink in an ocean of molecules. That would arguably be the end of science. The physical world can never be studied by something purely physical, any more than neurons could ever discover neurons! That is the reason why biology can never fully comprehend the human mind—biology itself depends on the working of the human mind.

A seventh reason can be found in information theory and information technology. Crucial in information theory is the separation of content from the vehicle that transports it. No possible knowledge of the computer's materials can yield any information whatsoever about the actual content of its computations. The brain supposedly works in the same way as a computer operates, since both use a binary code based on "ones" (1) and "zeros" (0); neurons either do (1) or do not (0) fire an electric impulse—in the same way as transistors either do (1) or do not (0) conduct an electric current. But that is where the comparison ends. Whatever is going on in the brain—say, some particular thought—may have a material substrate that works like a binary code, but it would not really matter whether this material substrate works with impulses, as in the brain, or with currents, as in a computer, for the simple reason that this material substrate only acts as a physical carrier for something immaterial—thoughts. This is like saying that a news report on the radio comes from an antenna, transistors, and a loud speaker. These do indeed help transmit the news, but they are certainly not the origin of the news—they simply do not determine the content of the news they broadcast.

Then there is an eighth argument indicating that the mental is different from the neural. It is based on an observation made by the philosopher Ludwig Wittgenstein. Picture yourself watching through a mirror how a scientist is studying your opened skull looking for "brain waves." Wittgenstein once noted correctly that the scientist is observing just one thing, outer brain activities, whereas the "brain owner" is actually observing two things—the outer brain activities via the mirror as well as the inner thought processes that no one else has access to. In order to make the connection between "inner" mental states and "outer" neural states, scientists would depend on information that only the "brain owner" can provide. The world of the mind is accessible only to the "brain owner." This is even so in court, in spite of lie detector tests; very often the only ones who know whether they did commit the crime or not are the defendants themselves. Lie detector tests detect not thoughts but at best physiological and emotional responses to those thoughts.

Apparently, there is no such thing as mind-reading through brain scans or other techniques. Contemporary neuroimaging techniques make it possible only to observe directly the *effects* of neurological activity, such as changes in intracranial blood flow. One cannot "see" cognitive activity itself, but only the effects of cognitive activity. Consequently, neuroscientists just cannot "read" a person's mind. If they want to associate certain brain activities with certain mental activities, they need to ask that person what he or she was thinking. Material explanations cannot possibly lead to a full understanding of non-material phenomena. Some speak of a "third-person ontology" versus a "first-person ontology." Neural phenomena have a third-person ontology, whereas mental phenomena have a "first-person ontology," being essentially subjective or "private," directly accessible only to the subject undergoing such mental experiences. No matter how we look at it, there seems to exist in this universe a dualism of properties—neural versus mental, objective versus subjective. The mind has distinct features—such as intimacy, privacy, first-person perspective, and unity of conscious experience—that cannot be found in the brain and its overt, public, third-person perspective.

A ninth argument could be found in the two components Aquinas distinguished in the human mind—reason and intellect (see chapter 4). While reasoning allows us to move from one thing known to another, the intellect can create concepts through the power of abstraction. Whereas the brain can handle signals and images, it seems that only the human mind can deal with symbols and concepts. Images can have some degree of generality—we can visualize a circle without imagining any specific size—whereas concepts have a universality that images can never have—the concept "circle" applies to every circle without exception. Because images are inherently ambiguous, open to various interpretations, we need concepts to give them a specific interpretation.

Mental concepts transform "things" of the world into "objects" of knowledge, thus enabling humans to see with their "mental eyes" what no physical eyes could ever see. Besides, the senses do not know themselves or their workings, but the intellect definitely does. Aquinas gives the following example: sight neither sees itself nor sees that it sees. The power of self-reflection or self-consciousness—knowing that you know something—belongs to the intellect alone. It is very hard, arguably impossible, to describe these phenomena in purely material terms. That makes it very questionable whether our understanding of the world is done by the brain. Augros uses the following analogy: You cannot count what you are seeing without using your eyes, but that does not mean your eyes are doing the counting. Similarly, it is clear that we cannot understand without using our brains, but it does not follow that our brains are doing the understanding.

Finally, here is a tenth argument. It does not seem very likely that thoughts can be induced in a physical way. We are not talking here about something like emotions or feelings (even animals have those), because those are physical and biological phenomena that can be physically induced by stimulation of certain brain areas. Neither are we referring here to memories stored in the brain—including memories of thoughts once produced by the mind—because memories can be physically stored, similar to the way thoughts can be "stored" on paper. Thoughts, on the other hand, cannot be produced in a physical manner, neither by chemicals nor by electrodes. If we could change beliefs with chemicals, presidential candidates would certainly consider that method in their campaigns. If the thought of "twelve times twelve" would physically produce the thought of "one hundred forty-four," we could have skipped much work in school. Unlike brain processes, which are subject to physical causation, thoughts are subject to mental causation based on reason and intellect.

Let us come to a conclusion. If one of the previous ten arguments convinces you completely, that is enough. If they convince you only partially, perhaps all of them together provide enough compelling reason for you to reject the idea that the mental is identical to the neural, that the mind is identical to the brain, or that the soul is identical to the body. Amazingly, many neuroscientists seem to have never heard these ancient and modern arguments. Or, having heard them, they have either forgotten them or discarded them. The truth is that mental events seem to transcend neural events to the same degree by which life transcends chemistry and physics. So now the question is what the status is of the mental, the mind, and the soul. Aquinas again has striking answers for us.

What Then Is the Mental If Not the Neural?

If the mental were the same as the neural, we would have an easy case of what is called *monism*, which reduces everything there is to one kind of entity—typically matter—which is the form of monism that materialism promotes. However, as the previous section indicated, there are very serious objections against this philosophical viewpoint. The term "viewpoint" seems to be appropriate here because materialism is a philosophical position; it is not a conclusion of the empirical sciences.

Besides, a monistic ontology contradicts itself, because the very claim of monism is a matter of cognitivity. Since molecules can make no claim to truth, any more than they can err, we seem to need a dualistic ontology that acknowledges cognitive events in addition to molecular events in order for us to make claims of a cognitive nature. This kind of dualism is usually expressed in pairs such as body and soul, body and mind, mental and neural. It may not be mainstream thinking, but some very sophisticated scientific and philosophical thinkers—such as the Nobel laureate and neurobiologist Sir John Eccles, the philosopher of science and religion Richard Swinburne, and the philosopher of science

Sir Karl Popper—are mind–body dualists who take the reality of the mental most seriously.

However, dualism creates its own problems. Descartes as well as Karl Popper and John Eccles maintain that events in the mind cause events in the body, and events in the body cause events in the mind—so-called interactionism. But the pressing question is how a material brain could ever carry out instructions given by an immaterial mind. As a matter of fact, many scientists would reject this kind, or actually any kind, of dualism. It is especially in Cartesian dualism that mind and body are seen as completely different entities—immaterial and non-localized versus material and localized—and yet they are supposed to interact—two different kinds of substances joined together in some mysterious way. As Alfred J. Freddoso puts it, this kind of dualism "destroys the unity of the human organism, positing an accidental composition of body and soul, neither of which draws its identity from the other."

In addition, Cartesian dualism fails not so much because of its dualism as because of its inability to explain how body and mind could possibly *interact*. Minds and bodies are not only different entities but radically different sorts of entities. How can a mind, a non-spatial item, ever cause effects in a spatial item, the body? This kind of dualism calls for a "medium," some sort of transmission process between mind and body. Locating this "medium" or "interface" in the pineal gland, as Descartes did, does not solve the problem, as a nonphysical mind cannot possibly contact any part of the body, not even a pineal gland. It is not surprising that Descartes's dualism has been characterized by the British philosopher Gilbert Ryle as a "ghost in the machine" theory.

This latter conception is connected with the so-called "homunculus fallacy," according to which consciousness is the work of the soul, or the mind—the inner entity that thinks and sees and feels and that is "the real me inside." When Descartes compares our minds to a pilot in his ship, he seems to suggest that our minds are the pilot behind our eyes and behind everything our body does. Critics reject this idea because it casts no light on the consciousness of a human being but merely redescribes it as the consciousness of some inner little being (*homunculus*). So these critics replaced this mysterious being with the monism of the brain. But as Max Bennett and Peter Hacker have argued, this homunculus fallacy keeps coming back in another form. Now the homunculus is no longer a soul but a brain, which is supposed to "process information," "map the world," "construct a picture" of reality, and so on. Oddly enough, this brings the homunculus back in a hidden way, for all these latter expressions can be understood only because they describe conscious processes with which we are already familiar. To describe the resulting form of "brain science" as an explanation of consciousness is therefore questionable, as it merely reads back into the explanation the feature that needs to be explained. It creates the unjustified impression that consciousness is a feature of the brain, and not of the person—a person being a unity of body and soul, mind and brain.

Aquinas would not agree with either monism or dualism. He would place the issue of body and mind in the wider context of the relationship between body and soul—with the mind being the intellectual part of the soul. In Aquinas's view, body and soul are not two individual substances, as in Cartesian dualism; rather, they are a unity whose nature is composed of both material *substance* and immaterial *form*, such that the body becomes what it is owing to the soul (and its mind). The soul is not taken by him to be "made up" of anything—it is not a kind of "stuff," it is not made out of "spiritual matter" (whatever that would be).

The fact that we distinguish body and soul does not entail that we can separate them, any more than the idea of a three-dimensional space means that we can separate those three dimensions. Body and soul make for a tight unity. The physicist James "J.C." Sanders puts it well: "Take away the soul but leave the body, and the body is a corpse; take away the body and leave the soul, and we have what we call a ghost." It is the form that makes a human being a human being. John Polkinghorne puts it in a different way: "If you take me apart you will find that all you get will be matter. . . . Yet if you want to encounter *me* you will have to refrain from that act of decomposition."

As a consequence, a human person must be seen as a unity of body and soul. Biology tends to isolate the body from the person, but the body is always a person's body. And the same should be said about the soul—it is always a person's soul. Ultimately, we cannot separate the body from a person, nor can we treat the soul as separate from a person. Yet, Descartes's view has permeated our culture by driving a wedge between body and soul. We tend to separate them and set them in an antagonistic relationship—a master/slave relationship. The body is often seen as a prison for the soul from which the soul wants to escape.

Tendencies to disconnect body and soul lead to dangerous consequences—such as the separation between sex and love, or between procreation and marriage. Some people, for instance, decide to undergo sex-change surgery because they have the feeling that their soul is "trapped" in a body of the opposite sex. Cases like these set the soul in opposition to the body; only the soul and mind are considered the "real me," thus leaving the body under full control of the soul. What gets lost in this approach is that body and soul are a unity, with the soul expressing itself through the body. There is no such thing as a disembodied soul here on earth.

Aquinas knows and accepts Aristotle's assertion in *De Anima* that it is as pointless to ask whether soul and body are one as it is to ask whether the seal and the wax are one—they unquestionably are. As the philosopher Stephen Priest says, "We could never, so to speak, peel thinking off the brain and discover metaphysical cement." Abstraction allows us to *tell* them apart but not to *set* them apart. So, on the one hand, Aquinas offers us a philosophy of dualism in the sense that he distinguishes the material from the immaterial; on the other hand, it is a philosophy of monism in the sense that the material and immaterial are tightly united so that one cannot be without the other.

Therefore, Aquinas does not have to struggle with the problem of dualism regarding how they interact, as Descartes did. Alfred Freddoso, for instance, asks some pertinent questions when it comes to what he describes as property dualism: "If correlated psychological and physical events are not identical with one another, do they bear causal relations to one another? If not, then exactly how are they related? What about the causal relations between psychological events and the physical events in general? Do physical events cause just other physical events, or can they cause psychological events as well? What about the other way around? Or are there two causally independent realms of events, the one physical and the other psychological?" All these questions remain difficult, if not impossible, to answer. The philosopher G. W. Leibniz solved the problem by maintaining that mental events and physical events are correlated but do not causally interact. He invites us to compare the operations of the mind and the operations of the body to two clocks, each of which keeps perfect time. This may seem like a smart solution, but it is not very attractive; it just invites us to further ignore the mental part.

Although, at first sight, the soul may seem an elusive idea, it actually is a very intuitive concept. It is the soul that makes us what and who we are. Our identities do not change when we gain or lose a few particles from the collection of particles that make up our bodies. John Polkinghorne is right: "The atoms in each of us are being continually changed by eating and drinking, wear and tear. They cannot be the source of our experience of a continuing self." Although my body changes constantly, I myself do not—that is, my identity remains the same. Most people would agree that we can change our cells and even our organs (through transplantation), but it is hard to change our personality. In a sense, the body is something we *have*, but it is more accurate to say that the body is also something we *are*. Even Descartes was aware of this, in spite of his dualism. At the end of his sixth Meditation, he says, "I am not only lodged in my body like a pilot in his ship but . . . so compounded and intermingled with my body that I form, as it were, a single whole with it." This makes the philosopher Stephen Priest state that, without this unity, the mind "would be aware of injuries to the body only at a distance. The soul would understand them as a pilot perceives damage to his ship." That is not the way the soul is aware of the body.

What then makes the living body just the sort of body that it is? The answer to this question in Aquinas's philosophy is the *soul*, but not understood in a Cartesian sense. To Aquinas, the soul is the substantial *form* of the living being. Body and soul or spirit and flesh, then, are two sides of the same coin, as form and matter are both necessary for any material object; indeed, the soul is the form of the body, or put differently, the spirit is the form of the flesh. Applied to the relationship between brain and mind—with the mind being the intellectual part of the soul—this would entail that the "form" of the mind gives a specific existence to the "matter" of the brain. The neural is not the same as the mental because the neural is "matter" and the mental is "form." But Aquinas would widen the distinction between brain and mind into a relationship between body and soul, for the brain becomes human because it is virtually present in a body with a human soul. No matter how difficult it is for us to accept ourselves as a composite of body and soul, Aquinas truly embraces the total reality of a human person as an organic composite of soul and matter without overemphasizing one element to the detriment of the other.

This makes the interaction problem of substance dualism disappear, because there is no soul "in" a body. The body "substantiates" the body and the mind, while the soul "in-forms" the body and the brain. In the Cartesian view, a pilot can be without a ship, and a ship can be without a pilot, but in the Thomistic view, there is no body without a soul (unless it is a corpse), and there is no soul without a body (except temporarily, as we will see below). It must be said, though, that Aquinas never connected the mind specifically with the brain. He does not take the brain as "the organ that we think with." It is modern science that has caused us to do so. Aquinas would rather speak of the intellect and the senses as a twosome. He keeps repeating that it is not my eye that sees, but it is *I* who sees; it is not my intellect that thinks, but it is *I* who thinks. We know things only through sensations, and yet we as persons are the source of these sensations. That's why the distinction between body and soul, between brain and mind, or between matter and form remains pivotal. The fact that an intoxicated brain cannot think well does not necessarily mean that the thinking comes from the brain. It may very well be that it is the mind that thinks, but does so through the *causa materialis* of the brain.

But no matter which terminology we use, Aquinas's analysis is in line with commonsense experience that tells us that body and mind are indeed intricately connected: An intoxicated body affects the mind, and a confused mind affects the body. Stress affects the brain, and headaches affect the mind. People with an optimistic outlook on life tend to be healthier and live longer than those who have negative thoughts. Placebos do have an effect that is called the placebo effect; it is a self-healing effect based on the *belief* that a "fake" medication or a "fake" treatment is the "real" thing. Examples like these show us that the unity between body and soul, or between brain and mind, is so strong that we can even speak of psychosomatic disorders that affect this twosome together. Aquinas considers body and soul, or brain and mind, to be so intricately united that the body can tell us something about the mind, and vice versa. So in a sense, Aquinas does acknowledge some kind of "mind-reading," for instance when he uses the example of the doctor evaluating a patient's mood through his or her pulse. This shows how closely body and soul are united. Brain scans may not reveal to us the actual content of someone's thoughts, but they do tell us something about what is going on in someone's mind.

As there is "in-formation" in DNA, there is "in-formation" in the brain—matter and form. Each comparison falls short, but asking how the mental makes the neural work is like asking how a computer program causes the computer circuits to solve mathematical equations. We should not take this as if the brain is the computer hardware and the mind the computer software, for that would be Cartesian mind–body dualism reborn. A computer does not create its "own" activities but merely executes activities preprogrammed by its designer.

Aquinas's view of the relationship between body and mind is actually state of the art; it could have been born in the age of neuroscience. His view is that the intellect is immaterial but sensation and imagination are not. Hence, it is no surprise at all that neuroscience has discovered various neural correlates of mental imagery and the varieties of perceptual experience. It is common knowledge that neural damage can affect even the functioning of the intellect. Most importantly, the soul—of which intellect, sensation, and imagination are all powers—is not a complete substance in its own right, but rather the form of the body. No wonder, then, that the mental matures when the neural matures. So the soul does not become united with the body, but the body becomes body through the structural principle of the soul. A human being is therefore an incarnated soul as well as an animated body. There is no such thing as a disembodied soul here in earth (more on this later).

But this does not mean that the "neuro" part of neuroscience is all there is to it. Norbert Wiener from MIT, for instance, at the dawn of information theory in 1948, spoke of a crisis in neuroscience: "The mechanical brain does not secrete thought 'as the liver does bile,' as the earlier materialists claimed, nor does it put it out in the form of energy as the muscle puts out its activity. Information is information, not matter or energy." Now, in-formation is a *causa formalis* concept, as stated earlier (see chapter 8). Recently, the cognitive neuroscientist Walter Freeman suggested that Thomism is the philosophical system explaining cognition that is most compatible with neurodynamics. Our mental capacities allow us to see possibilities that surpass the neural yet always need the neural to come to expression. Research suggests that the mind's mental states are also able to install new "programs" in the brain by creating new neuronal connections. Neuroplasticity is the key term for the flexibility of brain structures, based on the now-proven understanding that changes in behavior and environment actually alter the neuro-circuitry of the brain. The understanding of brain plasticity has replaced the formerly held position that the brain is a static and unchangeable organ.

On the other hand, we hear of new findings in neuroscience that seem to clash with Aquinas's philosophy of the mind. Many neuroscientists not only deny the reality of the mental, the mind, consciousness, and free will—they also think they have empirical evidence for their claims. Recently, for instance, experimental evidence was found that something like "free will" is just an illusion. I am referring here to Benjamin Libet's well-known experiments, which appear to demonstrate that so-called conscious decisions are already settled before we become aware of them.

This is what Libet did. He asked his experimental subjects to move one hand at an arbitrary moment decided by them and to report when the decision was made, which was determined by noticing the position of a dot circling a clock face at the moment of decision. In the meantime, the electrical activity of their brain was monitored. Earlier research had already indicated that consciously chosen actions are preceded by a pattern of activity known as a readiness potential (RP). If RP is indeed a measurable electrical change in the brain that precedes an act that we choose to make, RP could presumably be a good marker for a decision. Well, it turned out that the reported time of each decision was always a short period—some tenths of a second—*after* the RP appeared. This outcome seems to prove that supposedly conscious decisions are actually determined beforehand, but unconsciously.

Isn't that the end of the free-will debate? Perhaps not. There are many problems with this experiment. Without going into all the details, we should at least raise a couple of pertinent questions. First, one might argue that these experiments are based more on training than on conscious intervention. Experiments like these do not seem to represent normal decision making, as we do not typically make random decisions at a random moment of our choosing. Benjamin Libet asked his subjects to "let the urge [to move] appear on its own at any time without any preplanning or concentration on when to act." However, one cannot passively wait for an urge to occur while at the same time being the one who is consciously bringing it about.

This calls into question the status of the RP. In Libet's experiments, the experimental subjects were required to enter a frame of mind in which they were ready to make a decision at any moment. Perhaps the RP merely signals a quickening of attention, rather than a moment of decision. Whenever you have decided to do something, you know the decision has, by definition, already been made. In other words, the RP demonstrates that the expected brain activity always occurs before a decision but does not reveal the result of the decision. Any test that shows a delay just shows that subjects can indeed delay an action until after they have confirmed that they are conscious of the decision to act. How could we consider ourselves responsible for decisions we were not even aware of until after they had been made?

We are in fact dealing here with two different levels of awareness. It is quite possible that we need a certain amount of time just in order to report the awareness to ourselves. Being aware of having made a decision is one thing, being aware of that awareness is another—which might require more time to develop. The philosopher Peter Hankins worded it right: "The delay between decision and awareness does not mean the decision wasn't ours, any more than the short delay before we hear our own voice means we didn't intend what we said."

Then, there is a more fundamental problem. The subject in these experiments is not just at the mercy of impulses and urges. One has to realize that the subject chose in advance to translate the impulse into an action. However, the urge does not go directly to its goal without crossing the interval of consciousness. The philosopher David Bentley Hart makes a strong case here: we do not need electrodes on the scalp to tell us that we often feel an urge before we freely decide whether to act on it. The urge, however, is part of a wider mental context. Aquinas would say that impulses are merely the *causa materialis*, whereas the intellect that makes the choices is a kind of *causa formalis* that shapes impulses into intentional actions. There is no such thing as an isolated physical urge that exists wholly outside the free movement of the mind. There is no visible intentional content in any given electrical impulse that identifies it with any particular act. This Thomistic analysis of what is really happening here is rather different from what most neuroscientists want us to believe. Seen this way, the mind with its free will remains essential for shaping impulses into intentional actions.

All of the above is about a well-functioning brain. What would Aquinas's philosophy of the mind have to say about situations in which the brain is *not* functioning well? Would such malfunctioning affect the mind? In a way it would, because soul and mind are embodied entities. As William Shakespeare said in his *King Lear*, "We are not ourselves when nature, being oppressed, commands the mind to suffer with the body." To be sure, thinking presupposes a functioning brain, but it cannot be reduced to this fist-sized organ. But in another way, a malfunctioning brain would not affect the mind. A broken brain is as physical as a broken bone—but the mind is not physical, nor is the soul. Even people who have "lost their mind," as we say—whether it is through dementia, Alzheimer's disease, autism, or mental insanity—have not really lost their minds or their souls. The fact that they are human means that they have a human mind and a human soul. What they did lose, more or less, is a part of their brains, but not their minds. In other words, do not confuse a "defective brain" with a "broken mind."

Aquinas adheres to the following definition of man: man is a rational animal. This does not mean, though, that all human beings actually apply reasoning, or are even capable of exercising their power of reason. Brain injury or genetic defects might impede the exercise of this power. Just as mental capacities grow when we mature, so might they decline as we age. The brain not only enables the mind but also restricts the mind. Edward Feser uses the following analogy: that alterations to the body have mental consequences is no more surprising than the fact that altering the chalk marks that make up a triangle drawn on a chalkboard affects how well the marks instantiate the form of triangularity. Still, the mental power is always there to be impeded as long as we have a human being, for the power is *potentially* there. A severely brain-damaged human being is still the sort of being that will reason when there are no neurological or genetic defects. Contrast this with dogs, which never can reason even if they are healthy and whole, because this ability is not potentially there.

In Aquinas's view, human beings have specific potentialities and actualities (see chapter 3). This distinction is vital for assessing situations in which human beings are in a state of coma, brain damage, or dementia. Human beings with brain defects, like every other human being, are rational animals as a primary actuality with primary potentialities, as Edward Feser puts it. They have a first potentiality for speech, reasoning, thinking, and the like. When their brains are in good working order, they also have a secondary potentiality for these capacities. But when the brain is defective, although they lose this secondary potentiality, the first potentiality remains. That is precisely why the second potentiality would return if regenerative treatments were possible. Even if they seem to be in a "vegetative state," they still retain the potentiality that comes with a human being.

For that reason, ending a life in such a state amounts to destroying a human being, not a "vegetable." All in all, a person with a defective brain is neither a potential rational animal nor a former rational animal, but an actual rational animal who has been frustrated in realizing his or her potentials. Animals, by contrast, are never rational animals at all. They don't just "fail" to realize the potential for speech, reasoning, and thinking, because unlike even a brain-damaged human being, they never have those potentials in the first place.

Some might call this mere philosophical speculation. Interestingly enough, though, researchers at places such as the University of Virginia and the University of Vienna, Austria, are studying a phenomenon that has been called "terminal lucidity" —the unexpected return of mental clarity and memory shortly before the death of patients suffering from severe mental disorders. It is the term used when dying people who have previously been unresponsive or minimally responsive suddenly gain clarity of mind for a few hours, often talking coherently with loved ones before passing away a short time later. We know that there is no observable sudden change in the brain when death is very near. Is it possible, then, that the mind's sudden and short-lived return to normalcy just before death is brought about not by some inexplicable surge in brain functioning but by a regaining of the mind's potentialities? Examples include case reports of patients suffering from tumors, strokes, Alzheimer's disease, and schizophrenia. Although terminal lucidity has been reported for some two hundred and fifty years, it has received little scientific attention because of its complexity and transience—or perhaps because it doesn't fit into a paradigm that equates the mental with the neural.

This discussion may lead us to a related issue. How does the body-and-soul discussion apply to the rest of nature, outside the human realm? Aquinas actually assumes that all living beings have a soul—a specific form, that is. Plants have a vegetative soul, with growth, metabolism, and procreation; animals have a sensitive soul, with locomotion and perception; and human beings have a rational soul, with reason and intellect. These are "nested" in the sense that anything that has a higher degree of soul also has all of the lower degrees. All living things grow, nourish themselves, and reproduce. Animals not only have those activities, but they also move and perceive. Humans also reason, and do all of the above as well. Aquinas would even state that "the vegetative soul is in potency to the sensitive soul, as the sensitive soul is to the intellective soul." So there is a virtual presence of the vegetative soul in the sensitive, and of the sensitive in the intellectual. Therefore, virtual presence is naturally cosmological in scope; it is present in every part of the order of substantial generation, all the way up to the human being, the rational animal. Aquinas tells us that the intellectual soul "contains virtually whatever belongs to the sensitive souls of brute animals, and to the nutritive souls of plants."

Aquinas would even apply these three stages to the development of a human in the womb. It should not surprise us that this has led some people to the flawed conclusion that an unborn baby is a mere vegetable in its first stage, and a mere animal in its second, and finally a human being in its third—or to use our previous example, the flawed conclusion that a human being in a coma is back in a "vegetable state." The philosopher Jacques Maritain denied such a conclusion as follows: "It is a being which from the very first instant is made to be a man, and which becomes formally what from the very beginning it has already been virtually and by that fundamental life force on which it depends." Interestingly enough, embryology confirms that metabolism and growth appear before the sensory and neural systems develop, and finally the cerebral system matures. But that does not mean that the unborn baby goes through three different types of souls. It has a human soul with human potentiality from the very beginning. Since the embryo arises from a human mother and a human father, what species could it be other than human? The fact that most of us have reached an adult stage does not mean we are no longer the same person we were during adolescence.

Earlier we used the analogy of a monarch butterfly. We are in fact surrounded by substances that change their appearances. Most trees go through dramatic changes of appearance during their lifetime, and even during the cycle of each year. So we have a case here of accidental changes—one and the same subject may go through various changes, but it remains the same entity. It is not until the tree dies that a substantial change is taking place, because that very event removes the subject itself of accidental changes. Something similar holds for changes in a human being during the process from conception to natural death.

Can the Soul Exist Without the Body?

There is at least one more question that needs to be addressed: Can the human soul exist without the body? Because Aquinas agrees with Aristotle that body and soul make a tight unity and therefore cannot exist without each other, the answer seems to be "no." As a matter of fact, Aquinas readily admits, "It is clear that the soul is united to the body by nature: because by its essence it is the form of the body. Therefore it is contrary to the nature of the soul to be deprived of the body."

Does this mean that the soul cannot exist on its own after death? Not necessarily. Aquinas's philosophy cannot be understood without his theology. That is the reason why he departs from Aristotle at certain points. Well, here is one of those moments. Aquinas corrected Aristotle on this point, seeing in the soul the "form" of the body, but regarding it as a "substantial form" and therefore "subsistent per se," making it independent of the body in its existence. It is therefore of such a nature that it can subsist, even after the dissolution of the body of which it is the "form." This idea of an independent soul, in spite of its dependence on matter, may be on the verge of contradiction, but it is not as strange as it sounds. Think of the analogy of language: We can only think with and through language, yet our thinking surpasses language and is not absorbed by it, in spite of our dependence on language. In a similar way, although an incarnated soul is fully tied to matter, the very "act of incarnation" indicates there *is* something that "enters" matter.

Is this an inconsistent conclusion on Aquinas's part? Not necessarily. It seems to make sense that if the soul persists while the body keeps changing, the soul may also persist when the body is corrupted by death. Because the soul is immaterial, spiritual, and therefore simple—which means not composed of parts—it cannot be corrupted by its own nature, and therefore its capacity for immortality becomes a reality. Therefore, the human soul not only can be immortal, it really is immortal in Aquinas's view.

Nonetheless, although human reason tells us man is mortal—even if his soul (which is not the whole person) is immortal—it is contrary to the nature of the soul to be deprived of the body. Consequently, says Aquinas, when separated from the body, the soul is in a "violent" state, and the desire of the immortal soul is to be joined again with its own body. This is not required by human nature as such, since by his nature man is mortal—with his death "he dies," which ends his being a human person, even if his soul does not die—and therefore the resurrection of the body always remains a gratuitous gift of God that makes the person whole again. Although the immaterial soul survives a person's bodily death, the person that one is must necessarily be embodied.

Obviously, for human reason, death remains an impassible barrier: human beings cannot conquer death even if they are able to escape it through their souls. After death, a separated soul does not depend on the body for its existence, but it is no longer a (full) *person*. It is the soul's nature to be the formal element of a complete substance. Consequently, it does not have its own nature and is not a substance in its own right, even if it is capable of subsisting apart from the living body. It is because it is naturally incomplete in subsisting apart from the body that Aquinas sees the state of a separated soul as unnatural for it, and an opening—but not an argument, of course—for the resurrection of the body.

Is all of this mere speculation on Aquinas's part, or is there some neuro-scientific evidence that the soul does have the capacity to persist after the body breaks down? A possible confirmation might come from so-called near-death experiences (NDEs)—a broad range of personal experiences associated with impending death, encompassing sensations such as detachment from the body, feelings of levitation, total serenity, security, warmth, the experience of absolute dissolution, and the presence of a bright light. One of the first clinical studies of NDEs in cardiac arrest patients was done in 2001 by Pim van Lommel, a cardiologist in the Netherlands. With his team, he studied a group of Dutch patients who had been brain-dead from cardiac arrest but were successfully revived. Of the 344 patients who were successfully resuscitated after suffering cardiac arrest, sixty-two experienced "classic" NDEs, which included out-of-body experiences. Of these sixty-two patients, 50 percent reported an awareness or sense of being dead, 24 percent said that they had had an out-of-body experience, 31 percent recalled moving through a tunnel, and 32 percent described meeting with deceased people. Van Lommel concluded that his findings supported the theory that consciousness had continued despite lack of neuronal activity in the brain—a flat EEG. What such experiences suggest is that the mind and soul can survive brain death.

No wonder NDEs are often cited as evidence for the existence of the human soul. On the other hand, not surprisingly, all kinds of *biological* explanations have been suggested in reply: oxygen deprivation (anoxia), high carbon-monoxide levels, REM-sleep phenomena, psychedelic agents, hallucination. However, the question remains why not all people under those circumstances had NDEs. Besides, more research has been done to rule out these explanations. A recent study by Dr. Sam Parnia suggests that NDE patients are "effectively dead," having no neural activities that would be necessary for dreaming or hallucination. Additionally, in order to rule out the possibility that NDEs resulted from lack of oxygen, Parnia rigorously monitored the concentrations thereof in the patients' blood and found that none of those who underwent the experiences had low levels of oxygen. He was also able to rule out claims that unusual combinations of drugs were to blame because the resuscitation procedure (and thus the drugs involved) was the same in every case, and not every patient had an NDE.

As stated above, the soul is not a (neuro)scientific concept. It is Aquinas's philosophy that shows us that the human soul, which gives form to the body, is a substance that subsists by itself (*per se*), and not in virtue of some other reality such as the body. Therefore, it has not only its own reality but also its own independence from the body, to which it is substantially united such that it forms along with the body one being, a person. Therefore, a human being is not a purely material being, but a composite of spirit and matter—a spiritual being incarnated in matter. However, the spirit (or soul) subsists *per se* and therefore is able to exist without the body (or flesh). In other words, the soul is that part of us that lasts forever.

To open the mind for further study:

Ashley, Benedict M. *Healing for Freedom: A Christian Perspective on Personhood and Psychotherapy.* IPS Press, 2013.

Bennett, M.R., and Hacker, P.M.S. *Philosophical Foundations of Neuroscience.* Oxford: Blackwell, 2003.

Feser, Edward. *Philosophy of Mind.* Oneworld Publications, 2006.

Kenny, Anthony. *Aquinas on Mind.* Routledge, 1993.

11

Aquinas and Social Sciences

ACCORDING TO Aquinas, a human being is not only a rational animal but also a *social* animal. This is a dimension of Aquinas's thinking that may make his philosophy highly relevant for the social sciences. Let us find out how Aquinas could possibly provide the social sciences with a firm philosophical and metaphysical foundation or framework.

Before we do so, let me stress first that Aquinas does not see science as a value-free enterprise, as most social scientists see it nowadays, but rather as a value-laden endeavor. Perhaps it is possible to treat the physical sciences as somewhat value-free, but for the social sciences that is much harder to do. The discussion of whether science is value-free or value-laden has been very much influenced by the sociologist Max Weber. Weber was eager to stop scientists from having scientific discoveries tainted by their personal values. Personal interests do often guide the choice of research, but they should not affect its outcome. That was seen by many scientists as a very legitimate claim. But then Weber went astray by treating *moral* values also as a form of personal values, as if moral convictions are nothing more than personal, subjective judgments based on personal interests. Hence, he concluded that rationality—the hallmark of science—should leave no room for morality. Since then science, particularly the social sciences, is supposed to be free of values, including any moral values.

Many see this as an erroneous conclusion. Not only does it pose the question whether this very statement is more than a personal, subjective judgment on Weber's part, but it could also be traced back to a mix-up caused by the ambiguous nature of *values*. Values have something to do with the fact that we not only notice things and reflect on them, but also *evaluate* them—as beautiful or ugly, pleasant or painful, important or trivial, good or bad, and so forth. That is how we get personal values, family values, social values, corporate values, aesthetic values, economic values, monetary values, spiritual values, and last but not least, *moral* values. But these evaluations are not all of the same caliber. We cannot reduce all these values to values in the same sense in which money, for instance, has a value.

According to many philosophers, the moral values take a distinct position in the above list. They are connected with moral rights and moral duties, and they tell us what we owe others as a duty and what others owe us as a right. They tell us what we "ought" to do—no matter what, whether we like it or not, whether we feel it or not. Just as "truths are true," even when we do not know yet that they are true, "rights are right," even though we may not realize yet they are morally right. That's why science can be called "good science" in a double sense: "good" in terms of methodology and rationality, but also "good" in terms of morality. Science the way it was done in Nazi concentration camps may have been "good science" in the former sense, but certainly not in the latter sense.

Evaluating science as "good" in moral terms would give moral values a distinct status among all the other kinds of values. It sees morality as a search for universal obligations and objective values in this world. The term "objective" probably needs some further explanation. Usually we call something "objective" when it has been corroborated by scientific research and empirical investigation. That is not the sense, though, in which moral values are objective. Moral values are not the outcome of scientific research; instead, they provide the framework in which even scientific research takes place. The best social scientists can do is study with surveys and polls which moral values are prevalent in a certain society. But morality itself is not subject to science; it is the other way around—science is subject to morality. Not all scientific research that is technically possible is therefore morally permissible. Moral values are considered to be absolute ends in themselves—not disposable means to other ends. They are "objective" in the sense of being absolute and universal standards of human behavior—that is, unchangeable and nonnegotiable.

Those who object that moral values and laws are far from universal or absolute or objective, because they have been subject to change during the course of human history, seem to confuse moral *values* with moral *evaluations*. Moral evaluations are personal feelings or discernments regarding moral values. Making evaluations does not mean that we actually create moral values in accordance with such moral evaluations; it is the other way around—moral evaluations should be based on absolute moral values. Whereas moral evaluations may be volatile and fluctuating, moral values and laws are considered different from evaluations—they are timeless, universal, objective, and absolute standards that should guide our evaluations. As C. S. Lewis once said about moral values, "The human mind has no more power of inventing a new value than of imagining a new primary color."

Aquinas would think along the same lines. At least he points out that moral values are related to public interests, which go far beyond personal interests. Moral values, in his view, are a consequence of our responsibility for each other as human beings, which leads to moral duties and rights (more on this below). His keyword is the "common good" (*bonum commune communitatis*). It stands in opposition to self-interest and tries to counteract it. He does not understand the common good in an individualistic way—as the sum total of every person's self-interest bumping up against everyone else's self-interest, with the government serving as the referee. Neither does he understand the common good in a totalitarian way as whatever is best for the state. He also does not take it as the greatest possible good for the greatest possible number of individuals—which is not so good for the people who are not included in "the greatest possible number."

None of these interpretations are acceptable to Aquinas. Instead, he takes the common good as an *organic* conception: the individual is an organic part of society. Therefore, individuals cannot find fulfillment in themselves, apart from the fact that they exist "with" others and "for" others. In this view, the good of individuals is necessarily and intricately connected with the good of society. Thus, individuals are thought to attain happiness (a private good) through the pursuit of justice (a public good).

So be prepared: Aquinas will never leave moral values out of the discussion when dealing with sociological, economical, and political issues. Max Weber was right that personal values should not affect and taint the outcome of scientific research, but Aquinas would correct him by saying that personal values and interests are not identical to moral values.

Sociology

Let us begin our analysis with society as a whole. A human society seems to have decisive effects on the life of individuals. John Stuart Mill once demonstrated that it is never up to us to behave as we please, not even in the most liberal society. However, society does more than restrain individual actions. It also interferes with our thinking and feeling. Each individual life, for instance, is excessively conditioned by language. Well, language is thoroughly dependent on society. Additionally, the knowledge each one of us has is typically acquired by tradition and from hearsay—that is, it has come to us through society. Even personal emotions and desires are often a result of upbringing—that is, of the feelings and opinions that society at large expresses. No wonder society has always appeared as a power of intense actuality, as something "real."

Immediately, however, problems pop up. Looking around in our community, we perceive only human beings—individual human beings, that is. Terms such as "society" and "humanity" seem to be just simple collective terms for all, or certain, people combined; one never encounters a society as such. Although society faces us as a real and actual power, it cannot be situated anywhere; there does not seem to be such a "thing" in the world. Such considerations have persuaded certain philosophers and sociologists to voice the view that "society" is a pure fiction. They affirm that only individual persons exist in reality—a collection of autonomous, pure egos without any ties or connections. Some call this the Crusoe model of an "isolated man face-to-face with nature." However, this view raises questions of its own.

How can proponents of this kind of individualism—let us call them "individualists"—ever explain the evident fact that there is some kind of pressure that society seems to exert on each one of us, at least in the form of civil laws and the like?

The viewpoint of pure individualism, at least in its strict sense, has in fact very few proponents. Thomas Hobbes, Adam Smith, Max Weber, and more currently F. A. von Hayek and Karl Popper are individualists, at least in a methodological sense, because they think of individualism as the key principle regarding how to practice social science. Ayn Rand, who promoted the "virtue of selfishness" as well as a form of laissez-faire capitalism, could probably be considered an individualist in this sense too. Another representative, Ludwig von Mises of the Austrian School of economics, would also argue that only individuals act, and that society does not exist apart from the thoughts and actions of individuals, since society is supposedly nothing more than people cooperating, each to achieve his or her own individual interests. Society, in his view, does not have "interests" and does not aim at anything, so it is incorrect to say that individuals are working for the common good, because collectives do not have ends or desires. This view of society "atomizes" society, so that the single individuals act just as atoms and molecules in gases do. It leads to Thomas Hobbes's "war of all against all" and causes a man to be "a wolf to his fellow man."

The other extreme viewpoint in this discussion is that society is the one and only real entity, at the "cost" of individuals. Consequently, the individuals are seen only as parts of a larger whole and therefore do not qualify as complete entities. Just like the hand of a person is not complete in itself, but is only a part of the person, in the same way an individual person is only a part of society. As a consequence, individuals have no rights and duties of their own. After all, they live their lives as part of society, through the power of society, and for the benefit of society. The result is some kind of socio-ethical collectivism, ranging from authoritarianism (in which a single entity monopolizes political power) to totalitarianism (in which the regime attempts to control virtually all aspects of social life). What both views more or less have in common is that they turn citizens into a mere means to the sole end of advancing society—in the same way as ants and bees exist only to keep the colony alive.

Aquinas would take a middle position in this discussion. Because a human being is a *social* animal, individuals are real, but so is the society in which they live together. For Aquinas, living in society is not a pragmatic arrangement, but rather it is intrinsically necessary for man. God designed man so that this would be so. Therefore, social phenomena are the result of human beings evolving at both individual and social levels of organization at once. In this view, the society is more than the sum total of its individual members, with all of them having their own positions, responsibilities, and relationships within a larger entity.

Since human beings have a natural aptitude for living in society with others, they cannot attain their well-being outside of society. When one member is afflicted, all the others are affected. This calls for mutual responsibility and solidarity, instead of laissez-faire individualism, thus opening a middle road focusing on interactions between individuals within the setting of a society. Since humans are fundamentally social animals, rather than individualists, they have a natural tendency to create organizations beyond the individual—which are structures that range from nuclear families, extended families, and clans to cities, states, tribes, organizations, civilizations, cultures, and societies.

Aquinas would also stress that a human being is not only a social animal but also a *rational* animal. Because of this, a human being, unlike other creatures, is "master of his actions through his reason and will." Aquinas defines free will as "the faculty of will and reason." Free will gives humans dominion over their actions. Aquinas states that humans have free choice and "the intellect does not act or desire without forming a judgment." The judgments leading to choices that humans make are free because humans are in control of those choices. This is why we have thieves, liars, and kidnappers, but also doctors, nurses, judges, and teachers. Human beings are free to choose to act or not to act—and in choosing, they become causes themselves. People who do not care about what is right and what is wrong have *chosen* not to care; they have decided not to become a "good cause." Just as God has given us secondary causes and accepts their outcomes, so also He has given us free will and accepts our decisions.

Without an end in mind, humans would not act, since they would have no reason to choose an action. The end that they have in mind is what causes them to act, that they may achieve this end. Aquinas also says that humans use their intellects to identify their end and the means leading to the end. Although human beings are social animals, that does not stop them from also being rational animals. The most basic meaning of this statement is that human beings act for reasons: their deeds are intelligible by reference to their reasons. What makes human action real "action"—as distinct from mere reflexive "behavior" such as blinking one's eyes—is the presence of some mental reason, such as the reason behind winking at someone. Reasons, in this view, are not merely justifications for but also causes of action.

Clearly, for Aquinas, there is an important social dimension to rational human actions. He explicitly condemns the idea of individuals working for their own good in society. As he puts it, "In an earthly kingdom, peace ceases when the citizens seek each man his own." Aquinas views individuals working for their own ends as selfish and parasitic entities in society. Instead they should work for the common good—a key concept in Aquinas's thinking about society. Human beings come into this world with relationships, so separating them from these relationships is not an option for Aquinas. The individual good and the common good coincide. The common good cannot be properly understood without reference to the nature of the human person. The term "common good" names the end—or *causa finalis*—of life, both individual and social. So the common good can never be for the benefit of a few in society. When parts suffer, the whole suffers. No wonder some have said that this Thomistic conception is a liberation from imprisonment in self-absorption.

During the "Age of Reason" (the *Enlightenment* in English or *Aufklärung* in German), cultural and intellectual forces in Western Europe emphasized reason, analysis, and individualism. The socio-political philosophy of this movement generally rejected any such notions as the human person's natural sociability and orientation toward various common goods. Seen through the eyes of the Enlightenment, society exists above all to provide for the individual's comfortable self-preservation. Any remaining notion of a common good is therefore greatly watered down or replaced by the utilitarian ethic of "the greatest good for the greatest number of people." The focus is on safeguarding individual rights—rather than duties that contribute to the common good. In large-scale consumer societies, as Alexis de Tocqueville (1805–1859) predicted in his great work *Democracy in America*, individualism and materialism would become more acute and widespread. So the Enlightenment has left us a range of positions now—from individualistic liberalism, which makes the good of society yield to that of the individual, on the one end, to collectivism at the other end, which makes the collective good different from and higher than the good of its members.

As we mentioned already, Aquinas would reject these two extremes. The common good is the temporal welfare of the community. As a *collective* good, the common good is something over and above the good of individuals. As a *distributed* good, every common good must also come back in the form of benefits and goods for individuals. Extremists emphasize only one of these aspects to the detriment of the other—with collectivists emphasizing the collective aspect and individualists emphasizing the distributed aspect. Aquinas would again take a middle position. He makes it very clear that "the meaning of the common good and that of the singular good are different, just as the meaning of the whole and the part are different." It is something that unites individuals to their society, as organs are united to an organism.

The most obvious example of something that can exist only with the cooperation of two or more people is the family. The enduring union of a man and a woman is a "good" that is basic to the constitution of human life. Without the union of male and female, there can be no new human life. Without their further partnership in the bond of marriage, the new human life cannot develop properly as a person. Aquinas sees the family as the first "natural" society. It is a natural institution with a meaning that precedes any other social institutions. It is natural for two reasons: because the inclinations that lead us to create the family are very powerful, and because the family is the necessary context for the survival of an infant. Like society at large, the family is more than the sum total of its individual members, all of whom have their own positions, responsibilities, and relationships. Human beings need to be part of a family to be complete, and they also need society for the same reason. The individual family cannot be entirely self-sufficient; indeed, it relies on the surrounding community for its various needs.

Therefore, other levels of society, such as political organizations, no matter how rudimentary, may also be called natural, insofar as human beings have a natural inclination to form such societies and are unable to survive without them. But again, the whole is always more than the mere sum of its parts. Since we are social by nature, we need union with other persons in order for them to be who they are and for us to be what we are. But the family remains primary. Family is the fabric of society. When the institution of marriage breaks down, society suffers as well.

Economics

The preceding discussion about the philosophical status of society and of moral values necessarily affects the study of economics. If society is merely the product of individuals working together to achieve their individual ends and personal interests, then individuals will cooperate with others only when it is mutually beneficial to do so. In this view, cooperation also affects the division of labor. Pursuing their own interest, individuals trade with each other and specialize in their areas of efficiency. This makes for economic cooperation, but it is still fueled by individual actions that in turn are fueled by individual ends and interests.

Economists who take this position consider it a fallacy to speak of a society having goals or ends, because society is seen simply as a combination of individuals, each with his or her own ends. This view leads to what some call "Crusoe economics." A close adherent of this view is Adam Smith, who considers society as being guided by an "invisible hand." Though individuals act in their own self-interest, the result is that society benefits, and no government action is needed to ensure that the public interest is promoted. Private greed leads somehow to public benefit, says Smith.

However, if humans are by their nature social and moral animals, as Aquinas claims, then we should look at economics in a rather different way. In economic matters, Aquinas always views individuals as members of a society—not as individuals in isolation. Because he sees humans as social beings, he can compare the economy to a body, in which different members serve their respective functions. In his *Summa contra Gentiles*, he even uses the analogy of a beehive. One person cannot do all, and likewise, not everyone can do the same. This leads to a division of labor. But in all of this, Aquinas thinks that government is needed to regulate the economic activity of individuals: "For where there are many men together and each one is looking after his own interest, the multitude would be broken up and scattered unless there were also an agency to take care of what appertains to the common wealth. . . . Therefore in every multitude there must be some governing power." Thus, it is beneficial for society to have everyone serving his or her own productive purpose for the community as a whole.

The philosopher Aaron Taylor uses the analogy of the human body to explain Aquinas's concept of the "common good." It is clear that a healthy heart, for example, is per se something distinct from a healthy body. Yet the end of a particular bodily organ must be the same as the end of the whole body: health. Moreover, it is intrinsically necessary for the organ to be part of the whole body to attain that end. It is this organic conception of what constitutes the common good that was articulated by Aquinas. As a consequence, once we separate the individual from the community, the common good becomes a mere aggregate of individual interests or, worse, an uneasy compromise between conflicting sets of group interests and personal values.

With this background, Aquinas has a surprisingly good understanding of the economic ideas that economists rely on today, such as the law of supply and demand, subjective-value theory, and the theory of time preference. Aquinas views economic activity as falling into four categories: production, exchange, distribution, and consumption. However, we have to keep in mind that economics in the Middle Ages worked differently from how it operates in the modern age. Besides, we need to remember that most economists study economics as a value-free science, whereas Aquinas readily enters into a value-laden form of practical economics. Most, if not all, of the situations in which he addresses economic matters are in the framework of *justice*, with frequent reference to whether actions are "just," or morally right. In his own words, "The proper act of justice is nothing else than to render to each one his own." Because nowadays social scientists, including economists, attempt to conduct their study in a value-free manner, this approach has created a modern society in which "justice" and "good" are wholly subjective for the individual. Not so for Aquinas. His idea of justice is meaningless outside of society, because justice always deals with another person and can only be spoken of in terms of society. Justice is a matter of rights and duties, of what we owe others and what others owe us.

Let us see now how Aquinas deals with specific economic issues. First of all, *ownership*. Although Aquinas believes that nothing we have here on earth is really ours—since all of creation came from God—he also views property as necessary for human life: "[It] is lawful for man to possess property." Aquinas explains, in a very practical way, why goods owned privately are treated better than those that are owned in common. One reason for this is that man needs incentives to work, and private property, although not really belonging to the apparent owner, creates an incentive for people to work. Another reason is that transactions are more manageable when the responsibility lies with one person alone. Lastly, Aquinas says that contentment with private property brings about peace, while disagreements frequently arise over goods owned in common.

Another economic issue Aquinas deals with is *exchange* in terms of buying and selling. The only just exchange would be that of two identical goods for the same quantity, but this would be pointless; therefore, some value (an economic value, the price, not a moral value) would have to be established for the goods in order for the exchange to be just for both buyer and seller. He says that in buying and selling, the two parties exchange what the other wants. Aquinas recognizes that exchange is mutually beneficial. In such exchanges, however, Aquinas is careful to distinguish when the price is "just." Just exchanges must benefit both parties and not impose more of a burden on one than on the other.

What does Aquinas mean by "just price"? Some think that for Aquinas, the just price is simply the market price, determined voluntarily by buyers and sellers in an exchange. Others have interpreted Aquinas's just price as the price that sufficiently covers the costs of producing and selling a good. A third opinion suggests that Aquinas held that the just price is the "just person price," the price determined by just people. The economist Michael J. Hagan gives the following analysis.

In general, Aquinas would say that "price"—which measures the quality or economic value of a thing—is determined by how useful it is for us. The worth of a good, then, is subjective and determined by the consumer. Aquinas also realizes that a fluctuation of prices in the market is natural, because man's needs change over time. Thus, prices reflect the current value of a good according to its usefulness for man. But Aquinas adds explicitly that "the just price will depend not only on the thing sold, but on the loss which the sale brings on the seller." The just price, then, is specific to the situations of both parties of an exchange. The only person who would be able to understand his or her own and the other person's situation in light of justice is the just person. If so, Aquinas's just price is neither the market price nor the cost-covering price of a good. Rather, his just price is the price that is voluntary arrived at between two just persons who consider the good of each other in the exchange.

It should be noted, though, that there seems to be some inconsistency in Aquinas's ideas about price and economic value. He states that it is lawful to sell something for more than it is worth "in itself," although the price may not be more than it is worth to the owner. Thus, it appears that he is applying an objective-value theory (value "in itself") and at the same time also a subjective-value theory (how much something is worth to the owner). If a good has intrinsic value, the value is objective. If different people are willing to pay different prices for the same good at the same time, then value is subjective.

Since, in the real world, different people are willing to pay different prices for the same good at the same time, value is subjective, and there is no such thing as intrinsic value. Did Aquinas realize this? Whether he did or not, Aquinas was not alone on this issue; other thinkers of his day took a similar view of the just price. It was not until the last half of the nineteenth century that the subjective theory of value was first clearly stated. However, Aquinas did recognize the fact that market forces affect the value that is placed on commodities. Although this insight does not make him a subjective-value theorist in the modern sense of the term, it does show that he did not subscribe to the theory that all value is objective or intrinsic. This seems to suggest again that the just price is the price that is voluntarily arrived at between two just persons who consider the good of each other in the exchange.

One modern application in which we can see a violation of Aquinas's just price is "price gouging." This happens when merchants bring in supplies to those in areas of great need after a natural disaster and then sell the goods at a much higher price than usual. Such actions are commonly derided as taking advantage of the needy consumer. In Aquinas's own words, "To sell a thing for more than its worth, or to buy it for less than its worth, is in itself unjust and unlawful." Yet, in contrast to some early thinkers who dismissed all profit making as inherently unjust and sinful, Aquinas does recognize the societal benefits of trade and the need for a business to earn a "normal" profit and to be compensated for the risks that it took. Trade provides goods that would otherwise be either in short supply or nonexistent, so government should allow trade—but, he adds, should not encourage it. He believed that all gains made in trade must relate to the labor exerted by the merchant, not to the need of the buyer. His writings thus contain hints of ideas such as producers' long-run costs. What Aquinas is opposing is not trade or profit per se, but greedy profit seeking.

Another economic issue Aquinas deals with is the microeconomic principle of *supply and demand*. Unlike Aristotle and Augustine, who viewed trade negatively, Aquinas viewed it as neither inherently good nor inherently bad, but as potentially good. For him, trade itself is not evil; rather, its moral worth depends on the motive and conduct of the trader. He considers it fine to trade goods for a moderate profit, as long as one uses the profit to satisfy necessary or virtuous ends and not mere greed. On the other hand, the price of goods, according to Aquinas, must differ by location "on account of the difference of supply"— which is, again, not an intrinsic- or objective-value position. He plainly says, "Where there is greater abundance, the measures are wont to be larger." So a more abundant supply in one place will tend to lower price in that place. Consequently, Aquinas does not condemn the activities of merchants who make profits by buying goods where they were abundant and cheap and then transporting them and selling them in places where they are in high demand. None of this looks like a cost-of-production view of the just price. Rather, the just price is again the price determined by just people.

In his great *Summa*, Aquinas also touches on an issue that relates nowadays to *insider trading*. He uses Cicero's example of a merchant carrying grain to a famine-stricken area. He knows that soon other merchants will be following him with many more supplies of grain. Is the merchant obliged to tell the starving population of the supplies coming soon and thereby suffer a lower price, or is it acceptable for him to keep silent and reap the rewards of a high price? To Cicero, the merchant is duty bound to disclose his information and sell at a lower price. But Aquinas argues differently. Since the arrival of later merchants is a future event and therefore uncertain, Aquinas affirms that justice does not require the merchant to tell his customers about the impending arrival of his competitors. He could sell his own grain at the prevailing market price for that area, even though it is extremely high. Of course, Aquinas went on to say that if the merchant wished to tell his customers anyway, that would be especially virtuous, but justice does not require him to do so. This seems to indicate that Aquinas opts for the just price as the current price, determined by demand and supply, rather than the cost-of-production price. Or rather, again, the just price is the price determined by just people.

This analysis can also be applied to insider trading. Typically, a case of insider trading occurs when buyers with inside information call their stock broker and tell them to buy, knowing that the stock price is likely to rise as soon as the inside information becomes public. As stated above, according to Aquinas, there is no moral duty to inform a potential buyer that the price of the good one is trying to sell is likely to change in the near future. In other words, an insider who knows that the stock price is likely to change in the near future has no moral duty to inform potential buyers of this fact. And where there is no moral duty, certainly there should be no legal duty either.

Then there is the economic issue of *time preference*. This basically means that present goods are more valuable than future goods. Although the time preference theory was not developed until the late nineteenth century, Aquinas did recognize a crude form of it as applied to the just price. It is based on the fact that humans prefer their ends to be achieved in the shortest possible time, so they can satisfy their ends sooner rather than later. This explains why someone would be willing to pay interest on a loan. Aquinas's main objection would likely be that despite the buyer's preferences, the seller cannot charge for these time preferences because they do not belong to the seller. Again, Aquinas's goal is to establish justice, not to satisfy human preferences. Although he does recognize the issue of time preference, Aquinas still believes interest is unjust. Why?

Aquinas's primary argument against charging interest (*usury*) is that "to take usury for money lent is unjust in itself, because this is to sell what does not exist, and this evidently leads to inequality which is contrary to justice." So his argument against charging interest is that the lender is receiving income for nothing, since nothing was actually lent—only the money was exchanged. The main point that Aquinas makes here is that goods like money are consumed when they are used. Instead of using money to procure valuable goods, money lenders use wealth to create more wealth. Lenders who demand the sum lent plus a premium are acting unjustly because they charge for more than the use of the good. Any additional charge for money, says Aquinas, is either a charge on something that does not exist or a second charge for what was lent. In either case, the interest charge is unjust. The injustice arises because the lender is charging for something that is not his or her own.

Aquinas's ideas about interest may seem rather outdated nowadays. In order to understand his position, we need to consider where he comes from. Given the assumption that all things are created for their natural end, money is not an end but a means of buying goods and services. Lending money to others for the generation of more money is an evil unto itself. The formal value of money is the face value. Yet interest allows this face value to fluctuate, and hence the value of money can be diminished, thereby depriving the person who had purchased the money for use. Another argument with which Aquinas condemns interest is that of the distinction between consumable goods and non-consumable goods. Food and clothes are consumable—once they are used, they are gone—but a piece of land is non-consumable—it can produce crops for years, without losing its value. Since Aquinas defined money as a consumable good, it is not just to lend it to others for profit.

Aquinas's view of interest would prevail for the next three centuries following his death. The Council of Trent adopted his view of interest, calling usury a sin of equal gravity to that of homicide. This condemnation included putting money out for any return, no matter how small. It can be argued that this rigid stance may have encouraged Protestants and Jews to become involved in money trading and the formation of the banking system. The time of Aquinas was still one of land feudalism, but soon this land feudalism would make way for money capitalism. Over the next several centuries it became clear that capitalism would provide a greater amount of goods and services than any other system. Interestingly, the Islamic world—which forbids charging interest—still believes in the medieval view that charging interest is a form of exploitation. The Catholic Church also condemns usury as sinful, but the situation has become more nuanced now.

Although Aquinas did accept the time preference theory by recognizing that people prefer receiving something today rather than at some point in the future, he did not apply this to money lending. It is not surprising, then, that Aquinas's view has been revisited—mainly by making a distinction between usury and charging interest while "assuming a risk." Any time one assumes a risk, it is not considered usury to lend money to others and ask for interest. But when the lenders of the money do not assume any risk, it becomes usury, and the lenders become "loan sharks." This was the case, for instance, when poor tenant farmers and city dwellers were thrown into prison, or even killed, when they could not repay the money they borrowed and the interest charged. In these cases, the lenders did use money to gain a financial return, but they did so without assuming any risk. Although this interpretation was not Aquinas's view, it was still based on his concept of justice. It is obvious that his philosophy may not have all the answers to our current economic questions, but his principles remain timeless. Nowadays, we tend to see lending money to others as an act that benefits both parties of the transaction as well as a number of unidentifiable third parties such as workers and consumers.

Political Sciences

Human beings are understood to be not only rational animals but also *political* animals. That man is a political animal is based on Aristotle's thesis that the political community—the "city" (*polis*) in Aristotle's own idiom—coordinates the actions of persons and associations within it. This coordination of actions, practices, and institutions is usually included in the concept of "common good." Aquinas understands this concept yet again in the context of justice. He speaks of *distributive justice* and defines it as follows: "In distributive justice something is given to a private individual, insofar as what belongs to the whole is due to the part, and in a quantity that is proportionate to the importance of the position of that part in respect of the whole." Consequently, in distributive justice, people receive more of the common goods according to the position they hold in the community. In an aristocratic community, this prominence is gauged according to virtue, in an oligarchy according to wealth, in a democracy according to liberty, and in other ways according to other forms of community.

In 1267, Aquinas completed a work on government inspired by Aristotle's *Politics*. In this work, Aristotle reasoned, "Man is by nature a political animal." By this, he meant that people were naturally destined to live in groups, which require some sort of authority or government. According to Aristotle, only by living in a community "to secure the good life" could human beings achieve such virtues as courage, honesty, and justice. Aquinas affirmed Aristotle's stance: "It is natural for man, more than any other animal, to be a social and political animal, to live in a group."

Yet, Aquinas was not naive about people's actions toward the common good. He observed that people often tend to look only after their own self-interest. "Therefore," he concluded, "in every multitude there must be some governing power" to direct people toward the "common good." Thus, Aquinas saw government as helping society to work for the "common good" that benefits all. In his view, the common good included such things as protecting life, preserving the state, and promoting peace. Therefore, rulers not only have rights—to be respected—but also duties—to serve the common good.

The fact that man is by nature a political animal has far-reaching implications. In addition to being a father, a mother, a carpenter, or a nurse, a human being is more importantly identified as a *citizen*. Achieving genuine human excellence, therefore, means achieving excellence as a citizen of some political society. Whereas other animals such as bees exhibit a certain social tendency, only humans are social in the sense that they cooperate through speech to pursue a common understanding of justice, virtue, and the good. Since speech is the outward expression of their inner rationality, humans are political by nature for the same reason they are rational by nature.

Aquinas believes that a political society (*civitas*) emerges from the needs and aspirations of human nature itself. So it is considered an intrinsic predisposition, not an extrinsic invention of human ingenuity, as it is in the political teachings of modern social contract theorists. It is also not, despite the teachings of political theorists such as Thomas Hobbes and John Locke, an artificial construction designed to secure particular purposes and to make up for human nature's shortcomings. Rather, it is, in the words of the philosopher Peter Koritansky, "a prompting of nature itself that sets humans apart from all other natural creatures." So, political society is not simply a product of nature; it is something to which human beings naturally aspire. That is why the goal of the political community becomes the good of the whole, or the "common good," which Aquinas claims is "better and more divine than the good of the individual."

The concept of "common good" is based on rights and obligations; it involves actions that others owe us (our rights) and actions we owe to others (our duties). It adds a very different dimension to human social behavior. It is not tied to a special race, group, nation, party, or church, and it does not represent sectional interest groups; instead, it is something we all share. Just as our movements are subject to physical constraints, so also our actions are subject to social and moral ones.

Aquinas distinguishes a negative and a positive aspect of the common good. In a negative sense, the common good is the establishment and maintenance of order. When everyone knows what they are supposed to do, then individuals have the opportunity to act without hindrance and to develop as persons. Order provides the peace and harmony needed by society and individuals. In the positive sense, the common good "consists in giving to others and receiving from them powers and resources that as individuals none would possess."

It is obvious that in order for a society to reach its goal, *laws* are needed. Aquinas makes an important distinction between the natural law—which comes from God—and human laws—which are man-made. What does he mean by *natural law*? The master principle of natural law is, in his own words, that "good is to be done and pursued, and evil avoided." The notion of natural law presupposes the reality of nature—nature as something that is, though ultimately dependent on God, nevertheless distinct from God, such that it can be at least partially understood without reference to God. That is why we can know that certain actions are good for us and others bad, whether or not we know that the former have been commanded by God and the latter forbidden by Him.

Aquinas realized that the natural law is grounded in God's creation. Without God, anything is permissible—or at least we can make anything permissible by autonomously changing absolute moral values into our own relative moral evaluations. This latter position is called *relativism*. It was well defined by Supreme Court Justice Anthony Kenney in 1992 when he defended "the right to define one's own concept of existence, of meaning, of the universe, and of the mystery of human life." He worded a philosophical doctrine of relativism under the guise of a legal and political statement. Relativism declares us unable to know what is true and what is false, but also what is right and what is wrong—in spite of the fact that there are truths we want to fight for and rights we are willing to die for.

For Aquinas, the natural law is our participation in the governance of the universe that God brings about through the eternal law. The plan in God's intellect and will by which God orders the universe is the eternal law. Humans, by use of their reason, are able to understand the order through which God cares for everything in the universe, and in this way we discover the natural law—which is the reflection of God's eternal law "written" into our nature. Because the relation of rational beings to the eternal law is so different from that of any other created beings, Aquinas prefers to call the law that governs human beings by a different name. Therefore, instead of saying that humans are under the *eternal* law—as is all the rest of creation—he says they are under the *natural* law, and yet "the natural law is nothing else than the rational creature's participation of the eternal law." Another, equally accurate, way of stating Aquinas's position is that the natural law is the eternal law as it applies to human beings.

How do we know the natural law? How do we know what things are good—promoted by the natural law—and what things are evil—prohibited by the natural law? According to Aquinas, the very first precept is that "good is to be done and pursued, and evil is to be avoided." As he explains, this principle serves our practical reason just as the principle of non-contradiction serves our speculative reason. So it is a universal principle (see chapter 3). As Peter Koritansky asserts, "By definition, neither the first principle of speculative nor of practical reason can be demonstrated. Rather, they are principles without which human reasoning cannot coherently draw any conclusions whatsoever." In other words, they are first principles inasmuch as they are not derived from any prior practical or speculative knowledge. Still, they are as surely known as any other knowledge obtained through demonstrative reasoning. In fact, they are naturally known and self-evident for the very same reason that they are not subject to demonstration. Just as it is plainly evident that there is order in this world and that like causes produce like effects—there is just no hard proof for it—so it is equally evident that it is wrong to kill other human beings—there is nothing we can come up with in support of it.

This is how Aquinas knows that good must be done and evil must be avoided. But which acts are good and which are evil? In response to this, Aquinas argues that reason—a reflection of the mind of God—tells us more specifically what is good and what is evil. He states that "the light of reason is placed by nature [and thus by God] in every man to guide him in his acts." Human beings are the only ones among God's creatures who use reason to lead their lives. Reason tells us what is good and what is evil. In other words, the natural law comes directly from God; without God, there is no natural law.

Reason reveals to us not only what is good—such as self-preservation, marriage, family, and the desire to know God—but also what is evil—such as adultery, suicide, murder, and lying. This is natural law. In general, the natural law is the same for all people and can be known by all people. What God commands, through our human nature, is always and everywhere the same. Interestingly enough, Isaac Newton once stated, "There is but one law for all nations: the law of righteousness and charity dictated to the Christians by Christ, to the Jews by Moses, and to all mankind by the light of reason."

It is Aquinas's view that the natural law—that which God commands us to do—can be known by everyone through our natures—which means everyone can know what we *ought* to do from the way we *are*. Nowadays, under the influence of David Hume and more recently G.E. Moore, this way of thinking has come under attack as violating the rule that we cannot derive what ought to be done from the way things are—"ought" does not flow from "is"—and that moral properties are different from natural properties. Survival of the fittest, for instance, may be the way it *is* in nature, but we cannot infer from this that it *ought* to be that way in a human society. This has become known as the rule that "ought" cannot be derived from "is"—otherwise we commit the so-called "naturalistic fallacy." The philosopher Jeremy Bentham, for instance, criticized natural law theory because in his view it is a naturalistic fallacy, claiming that it derives how things ought to be from the way things are.

In response to this attack on Aquinas, Ralph McInerny explains that "ought" is already bound up in "is," insofar as the very natures of things have ends or goals within them. A clock, for example, is a device used to keep time, so because it "is" a clock, it "ought" to keep time. In like manner, if one cannot determine good human action from bad, then one does not really know what the human person *is* by nature. In a similar vein, Pope Emeritus Benedict XVI reiterated recently the Thomistic view that "the ought does flow from the is." What he meant is that once we get a sense of who God *is* and what a human being *is*—created in God's image and likeness—certain *oughts* do flow from that.

Closely connected with the natural law is the concept of *conscience*. Although it is not directly a political issue, it deserves some explanation here. Ironically, even moral relativists hold on to at least one moral absolute that says, "Never disobey your own conscience." So we should then ask them where the absolute authority of a human conscience could possibly come from. Do my genes, or any other natural factors, have the right to demand absolute obedience from me? Does society have the right to demand my absolute obedience? Does any person, including myself, have the right to demand my absolute obedience? Most likely, none of the above! The only authority that can obligate me is something—or rather someone—infinitely superior to me; no one else has the right to demand my absolute obedience.

That is where the natural law comes in again. The individual's conscience does not speak on its own but merely reflects the natural law revealed to us by God. Our conscience does not create moral laws but merely receives them. That is the reason why we cannot take our conscience as an entirely private issue and as something that we can form at our own discretion. Therefore, one's moral judgment doesn't become true by the mere fact that it has its origin in conscience, because a conscience needs to be truthfully formed first so as to echo or reflect the natural law. As said earlier, personal moral evaluations do not necessarily reflect universal moral values.

Aquinas believed that it is one faculty, the intellect, that has insight, at least potentially, into truths of any kind, whether "moral" or "nonmoral." As a practical moral judgment, conscience takes the form "I ought to do X." Aquinas points out that when we make such a judgment, we ought to follow it. Conscience is a judgment—a judgment that can be either correct or erroneous, since we are no more infallible in moral judgments than in any other kind of judgment. Although conscience is fallible, it is nonetheless binding. This leads Aquinas to a rather unexpected conclusion. The persons who deliberately do what they are convinced is wrong, or fail to do what they are convinced is obligatory, actually commit a sin. Thus if one's intellect conceives of a certain good action—say, a blood transfusion—as bad, one's will becomes bad by choosing the action believed to be bad. In other words, to act against one's conscience, even against an erroneous conscience, is bad. This conclusion of Aquinas has often been hailed by some as proclaiming the absolute authority of someone's private conscience.

However, as the Dominican Thomas Crean points out, the opposite doesn't necessarily follow—that is, to act in accordance with an erroneous conscience is not necessarily good and praiseworthy. It depends on what led one to have an erroneous conscience in the first place. The error itself could be culpable, in which case the actions that flow from it will also be culpable. For example, doctors who think that they should perform an abortion for a woman when she asks for it may be acting in accordance with their conscience, but their conscience is gravely in error and their error is culpable, since it bears on a precept of nat-

ural law that everyone can and should know, namely, that inno-
cent human beings are not to be killed. Since conscience is both
binding and fallible, it is clear that we have a duty to educate and
inform our conscience properly. In other words, acting on one's
conscience is not enough. Like any other kind of judgment, we
base our moral judgments not only on principles but also on evidence, data, and information. The main source of these is the
natural law. Thus, Aquinas considered it important to form one's
conscience properly.

Because of this, we need to make a distinction between "what
is good" according to the natural law and "what is *considered*
good" in the minds of some—which leads again to an important
distinction between values and evaluations. Moral evaluations
are our personal feelings or discernments regarding moral values. Moral evaluations may change, but moral values do not,
because the natural law does not change. Moral values are not
subject to various cultural and historical fluctuations and should
not depend on emotions, personal preferences, sectional interests, cultural trends, political powers, or majority votes. Whereas
moral evaluations may be volatile and fluctuating, moral values
and laws are eternal, universal, objective, and absolute. Think of
the following comparison: Our current understanding of physical
or biological laws needs revision each time we reach a better
understanding of those laws in the way they really are. Something similar holds for the natural law. The natural law is intrinsically right, even when we do not see yet that it is. Just as there are
color-blind people, there are also value-blind people.

In addition to the natural law, Aquinas identifies man-made laws.
While natural law applies to all humans and is unchanging,
human law may vary with time, place, and circumstance. Aquinas
defined this latter type of law as "an ordinance of reason for the
common good" made and enforced by a ruler or government.

Human laws serve two purposes. First, they provide the missing details that the natural law leaves out owing to its generality.
Second, they compel those under the law to observe standards of

justice and morality, including those which the natural law specifies. For Aquinas, the rule of law is ultimately a matter of doing what can be done to see that the state is ruled by "reason, that is by law which is a prescription of reason, or by somebody who acts according to reason"—rather than, as he says, by "men, which is according to whim and passion."

One might think that Aquinas would define *human* law as what is often called nowadays *positive* law—the civil laws actually enacted and put in force by a specific political community. The reason for not equating them is that Aquinas applies his four types of causality to all human laws for further evaluation: a law's material cause is the public promulgation of the law; its efficient cause is the proper authority to promulgate the law; its final cause is the common good of the people; and last but not least, its formal cause is a precept of reason in accordance with the natural law. According to Aquinas, if a law is missing any of these four causes, especially the last one, it is not a law—at least not a "just law." As a consequence, citizens are not bound to obey laws made by humans that conflict with the natural law. The natural law surpasses all human laws.

As a matter of fact, without Aquinas's distinction between the natural law, on the one hand, and human laws or positive laws or civil laws, on the other hand, there would not have been any justification for the Nuremberg trials that took place after World War II—or for any other international court, for that matter. Seen from a purely legal point of view, it would not have been right, or even possible, to bring to trial and punish the Nazi perpetrators who had applied the laws that were created and implemented by a regime that had come to power through legal channels—for they were just law-abiding citizens following the law of the land. But seen from a natural law perspective, their "lawful" actions were atrocities committed against humanity.

The natural law represents the metaphysical order that dwells in all of creation and is the only solid base for individual and social moral life. Although the Nuremberg court never referred to natural law directly, in essence it was the deciding factor. The court posed a pivotal question: Is there some superior law, or are there superior laws, to which even the properly enforced laws of nations are subject? In the mid-twelfth century, the canon lawyer Gratian had already put it concisely: "Law is what is just," not the opposite, "Justice is what is law." To put it differently, some things can be legal but are immoral, such as adultery, bribery, and price gouging. And some things are moral but are considered illegal in certain legal systems, such as abolition of slavery or free expression of faith.

An interesting case in point comes from Thomas More, a highly successful practitioner of law and chancellor of England under Henry VIII. When the king wanted More to support him in his desired divorce from Queen Catherine and in his proclamation ordering the clergy to acknowledge him as the supreme head of the Church, More rejected both these contentions. Hence, he was tried for treason, found guilty, and executed. His last words were, "The King's good servant, but God's first." More was, indeed, a martyr for his belief that natural law supersedes the law of the state. Law, to be considered as law that can command obedience, must be just, must be in accordance with the natural law, which, in turn, enjoys divine sanction. In his book *Utopia*, the reader gets a glimpse of More's version of natural law when he writes that the Utopians "define virtue as living according to nature." Then More concludes by asking, "And is it just for a government to ignore the welfare of farmers, charcoal burners, servants, drivers, and blacksmiths, without whom the commonwealth could not exist at all?" The lawyer Thomas More believed in the supremacy of the natural law. It was his conviction that there were things that no parliament could do—for example, no parliament could make a law that God should not be God. The end and purpose of all laws is justice and a just society.

Someone who also realized very clearly that positive, civil laws may actually violate the natural law was Martin Luther King Jr. In his 1963 *Letter from Birmingham Jail*, he declared, "There are just and there are unjust laws." And then he goes on, "I would agree with Saint Augustine that 'An unjust law is no law at all.' . . . A just law is a man-made code that squares with the moral law or the law of God. An unjust law is a code that is out of harmony with the moral law." Then King goes on, "To put it in the terms of Saint Thomas Aquinas, an unjust law is a human law that is not rooted in eternal and natural law." The importance of the theory of natural law is that it affords the possibility of "rebellion"; it provides a court of appeal, for without it there would be no court of appeal beyond the edicts of people.

In other words, when we are speaking of natural law, we are in the field of morality rather than in that of legality. Human laws are "under" the natural law—or at least should be. Political authority is binding only if it conforms to natural law, divine law, and the common good of the community—otherwise, governments become tyrannical. As Frank Sheed, a lawyer and founder of the publishing house Sheed and Ward, once put it, "The only alternative to the rule of law is the tyranny of the strongest." Therefore, in line with Aquinas, Sheed stressed the distinction between society and the state—society is larger and precedes the state, which is the organized form of society. In his own words, "The unit of Society is a man, of the State a citizen; and a man is more than a citizen."

So this raises the question of what citizens should do about a *tyranny* that makes its own human laws. Aquinas agreed with Augustine that the subjects of unjust rule are not obliged to obey those laws that are not legitimate. Aquinas argues that the subjects of a tyranny, acting as a "public authority," might rebel and depose it. He cautions, though, that no one should do this hastily, but only when the damage done by the tyranny exceeds what may occur in a rebellion. This was one of the first justifications for revolution in Western thought.

Another issue that is closely connected with the concept of natural law is the concept of human *rights*. It is arguably the philosophy of Aquinas—or at least his natural law philosophy—that gave rise to the idea of human rights, the recognition of the inviolability of human dignity in every single person, and the awareness of people's responsibility for their actions. The United States Declaration of Independence acknowledges this as well by stating explicitly that human rights are God-given rights: "We hold these truths to be self-evident, that all men are created equal, that they are endowed by their Creator with certain unalienable Rights, that among these are Life, Liberty and the pursuit of Happiness." Its framers realized that human equality cannot rest on qualities such as wealth, virtue, and intelligence—which are very unequally distributed among us—but instead is given to us by the Creator. The laws of the state are to be judged by the standards of justice—that is, the natural law. President John F. Kennedy put it well in his inaugural address: "The rights of man come not from the generosity of the state, but from the hand of God."

Then, in 1948—after World War II, when the first photographs of inhumane atrocities in the Nazi concentration camps appeared—the UN affirmed in the Universal Declaration of Human Rights that "all human beings are born free and equal in dignity and rights." Whether the UN members realized it or not, they were implementing and enforcing some form of natural law. Besides, they were implicitly proclaiming that rights must come from God—otherwise all those rights would be sitting on quicksand, subject to the whims of lawmakers and majority votes.

Without God, we would have no right to claim any rights. If rights really come from human beings, and not God, human beings can take them away at any time—and they certainly have tried to do so and will try again. Even an atheist such as the French philosopher Jean Paul Sartre realized that there can be no absolute and objective standards of right and wrong if there is no eternal heaven that would make the natural law objective and universal. As an atheist he had to assert, though, that it is "extremely embarrassing that God does not exist, for there disappears with Him all possibility of finding values in an intelligible heaven. There can no longer be any good a priori, since there is no infinite and perfect consciousness to think it." One could easily pose the rhetorical question, "How can there be absolute moral laws if there is no eternal moral Lawgiver?"

Once we lose sight of the special status of rights—which are based on natural law—the concept of *rights* becomes entangled with the concept of *entitlements*—derived from positive laws. Some people think of human rights as if they are entitlements that the government gives us. But there is a fundamental difference between these two. We gain entitlements as we age—according to the laws of the land, we can drive a car at sixteen, we can vote at eighteen, we can buy alcohol at twenty-one. But we cannot apply this kind of reasoning to human rights. A human being does not gain more rights as it progresses further along the path toward being born. Protection of a human being is not a conditional legal entitlement, but an unconditional moral right. It does not progress with age, but is rooted in the fact that we are dealing with a human being from the very beginning. There is no gradualism when it comes to human rights; killing a twenty-year-old is not different from killing a fourteen-year-old.

When we fail to distinguish between rights and entitlements, we are in for serious trouble. A right is based on natural law, whereas an entitlement is a legal notion based on positive law. Rights are God-given, whereas entitlements are man-made. We have rights because all human beings are God's creatures subjected to his natural law; entitlements we have only because we belong to a certain society. Rights are God-given rights that we cannot invent on our own, but entitlements are something that individual societies regularly invent and promulgate. The government can hand out entitlements, but not rights; although the government cannot bestow rights, it may sometimes try to take them away.

Rights and duties go hand in hand—they have a reciprocal relationship. Rights are what others owe us; duties are what we owe to others. If there are no duties, then there are no rights. To give a few examples: there is no duty to own slaves, so there is no right to own slaves; there is no duty to die, so there is no right to die; no duty to marry, so no right to marriage; no duty to have children, no right to have children. Once we uncouple rights from duties, fake new "rights" can pop up like mushrooms. They are invented and claimed on the spot, but the question of duty is utterly lost. At best they can become entitlements, enforced by a legal system—the laws of the land, so to speak. Entitlements are at most something the government owes us, but not something we owe the government.

A separate issue discussed by Aquinas extensively is the idea of just and unjust wars in relationship to the political common good. Aquinas further developed the meaning of *just war* that had been discussed by the Roman statesman Cicero and by Augustine. For a war to be just, these three conditions must be met: (1) a declaration by the ruler to defend the "common good" against enemies, (2) a "just cause" for an attack on an enemy, based on the fact that the enemy deserves to be attacked on account of some fault, (3) a "rightful intention" to advance good or avoid evil, such as punishing evildoers, not simply grabbing land or goods. These three conditions for a just war were well articulated by Aquinas and would later influence the development of international laws of war.

To open the mind for further study:

Cessario, Romanus. *Introduction to Moral Theology.* Catholic University of America Press, 2001.

Di Blasi, Fulvio. *God and the Natural Law: A Rereading of Thomas Aquinas.* South Bend, IN: St. Augustine's Press, 2006.

Hagan, Michael J. "St. Thomas Aquinas: Economics of the Just Society." http://www2.gcc.edu/dept/econ/ASSC/Papers2013/ASSC2013-HaganMichael.pdf

Koritansky, Peter. *Thomas Aquinas and the Philosophy of Punishment.* Catholic University of America Press, 2011.

McInerny, Ralph, and O'Callaghan, John. "Saint Thomas Aquinas," *Stanford Encyclopedia of Philosophy* (Spring 2005 edition), Edward N. Zalta (ed.). http://plato.stanford.edu/archives/spr2005/entries/aquinas/

Porter, Jean. *Nature as Reason: A Thomistic Theory of the Natural Law.* Wm. B. Eerdmans Publishing Co., 2004.

Sheed, Frank. *Society and Sanity: Understanding How to Live Well Together.* San Francisco, CA: Ignatius Press, 2013.

Stump, Eleonore. *Aquinas.* Routledge, 2005.

Conclusion

THERE IS NO denying that Aquinas has had an enormous influence on our Western civilization, but it can also be said that he indirectly shaped the way the various sciences would develop. Although his philosophy has been rejected by some modern scientists—most likely through lack of knowledge about Aquinas's work—the preceding chapters are an attempt to demonstrate how helpful his ideas, concepts, and distinctions can be in analyzing and assessing the discoveries that scientists have made. Time is always the best judge of what a particular philosophy is worth.

Is Aquinas's philosophy perfect? Of course, it is not. Did Aquinas make mistakes? Of course, he did. But they are dwarfed by his marvelous and timeless insights and accomplishments. He himself would be the first one to acknowledge his own limitations. What he said about all human judgments—that they can be either correct or erroneous—he would also apply to his own rational and intellectual judgments—they are no more infallible than any other kind of judgment. If all those who declare his philosophy erroneous could acknowledge their own shortcomings as much as he did, there would at least be an opening for further dialogue.

On his deathbed, Aquinas humbly spoke to God, "Thee have I preached. Thee have I taught. Never have I said anything against Thee. If anything was not well said, that is to be attributed to my ignorance." I would like to say the same about the contents of this book.

INDEX

Index

ether 112, 115
explanation 44

faith and reason 13, 22–24, 26
falsification 75, 81, 119
Faraday, Michael 112
Feser, Edward 5, 19, 30, 47, 49,
    117, 121, 124, 196, 202
Feyerabend, Paul 19
Feynman, Richard 16
field 98, 112–14, 122
fitness 141, 157–58
Five Ways 51–52
form and matter 36, 39–40, 190
Frankl, Victor 180
Freddoso, Alfred J. 187, 189
Freeman, Walter 4, 193
free will 179, 193–95, 208–09

Galileo Galilei 25–26, 81
gene 64, 70, 127–29, 136–42, 148–
    54, 157, 160, 167, 179, 224
    duplicates 141, 149–50 167
    selfish 152
Gilbert, Walter 133
Gilder, George 134–35
Gilson, Etienne 12, 158
government 205, 211–12, 215, 219–
    20, 226, 228–31
Grand Unified Theory 98
Grant, Edward 88–89
gravitation 82, 97, 107, 109, 111,
    113–14, 119
gravity 44, 48–49, 71, 93–96, 98,
    101–02, 111, 114, 152
Greene, Marjorie 136
Grosseteste, Robert 81

Hacker, Peter 188, 202

Hagan, Michael 214, 232
Haldane, John 59, 137
Hankins, Peter 195
Hannam, James 89
Hart, David Bentley 195
Hawking, Stephen 27, 94–97, 99,
    102, 174–75
Heidegger, Martin 28–29
Heisenberg, Werner 4, 116, 123
Heraclitus 34
heterozygote 127
Higgs boson 71, 99, 104, 174
Hill, James 61
Hobbes, Thomas 207, 220
homozygote 127
homunculus fallacy 187–88
Hoyle, Fred 93, 174
Human Genome Project 129, 142
Hume, David 18, 55–62, 76, 164,
    223
Husserl, Edmund 62
hypothetical reasoning 67, 82

imagination 70, 143, 192
immortality 200
indeterminacy 117, 120, 123, 125
indeterminism 120
individualism 207–10
inertia 82
information 7, 9, 17, 63, 65, 107,
    120, 124, 133–39, 142
information theory 183, 193
intellect 23, 35, 58, 62–65, 67, 147,
    170, 184–86, 188, 191–92, 195,
    197, 209, 225
    vs. intelligence 69
intelligence 21, 68–69
    in nature 171
Intelligent Design Theory 171
interactionism 187

237

About the Author

Gerard M. Verschuuren is a human geneticist who also earned a doctorate in the philosophy of science. He has studied and worked at universities in Europe and the United States. Currently semi-retired, he spends most of his time as a writer, speaker, and consultant at the interface of science and religion, faith and reason.

Some of his most recent books are the following:

Darwin's Philosophical Legacy: The Good and the Not-So-Good. Lanham, MD: Lexington Books, 2012.

God and Evolution? Science Meets Faith. Boston: Pauline Books, 2012.

What Makes You Tick? A New Paradigm for Neuroscience. Antioch, CA: Solas Press, 2012.

The Destiny of the Universe: In Pursuit of the Great Unknown. St. Paul, MN: Paragon House, 2014.

It's All in the Genes! Really? Charleston, SC: CreateSpace, 2014.

Five Anti-Catholic Myths: Slavery, Crusades, Inquisition, Galileo, Holocaust. Kettering, OH: Angelico Press, 2015.

Life's Journey: A Guide from Conception to Growing Up, Growing Old, and Natural Death. Kettering, OH: Angelico Press, 2015.

For more information: http://en.wikipedia.org/wiki/Gerard_Verschuuren. The author can be contacted at www.where-do-we-come-from.com.

Made in the USA
Middletown, DE
07 November 2019

78253756R00149